D1590573

The Drug Scene

in Great Britain

'Journey into Loneliness'

The Drug Scene

in Great Britain

'Journey into Loneliness'

Max M. Glatt
David J. Pittman
Duff G. Gillespie
Donald R. Hills

London

Edward Arnold (Publishers) Ltd.

© Max M. Glatt, David J. Pittman, Duff G. Gillespie,
and Donald R. Hills 1967

First published 1967
Revised reprint 1969

178.8
D-74
c.2

HV
5840
.G7
D7
1967

SBN: Boards 7131 4124 7
SBN: Paper 7131 4127 1

Printed in Great Britain by
William Clowes and Sons, Limited, London and Beccles

72-4741

Contributors

MAX M. GLATT, M.D., D.P.M.
Consultant Psychiatrist, St. Bernard's Hospital, Southall
Member of the WHO Expert Advisory Panel on Drug
Dependence
Hon. Editor British Journal of Addiction

DAVID J. PITTMAN, Ph.D.
Director of the Social Science Institute, and Professor of
Sociology, Washington University, St. Louis, Missouri

DUFF G. GILLESPIE, M.A.
Fellow, Social Science Institute, Washington University, St.
Louis, Missouri

DONALD R. HILLS
Honorary Research Assistant, Alcoholism Addiction Unit,
St. Bernard's Hospital, Southall

Preface

The sub-title, *Journey into Loneliness,* of this study of the drug scene and subculture in Great Britain derived from a drug addict's description of his experience with drugs. In describing his addiction the patient stated that 'going on drugs is like a journey into loneliness'. This short phrase perhaps more than any other captures the personality dynamics of the drug user and the essence of the subculture. Many youngsters, both in Great Britain and the United States are attempting to find a sense of identity and a relationship to the events of the world that surrounds them. In this quest some turn to drugs in a search for short-cut answers.

This volume is the outcome of a collaborative effort which not only crosses the boundaries of psychiatry and sociology, but also of nations, Britain and the United States. Many people in the United States, worried about the high incidence of drug addiction in their country, had looked hopefully to the permissive 'British system' for a solution, as it was felt that the fact that British general practitioners were allowed to prescribe heroin to addicts would prevent consequences such as the spread of addiction, the emergence of a black market, and so on. However, as illustrated in this volume, things in Britain have not worked out in that way.

We wish to express our deep appreciation for the excellent editorial and administrative aid of Mrs. Ruth Bruce and Mrs. Phyllis Buffam. We also appreciate the cooperation of the drug addicts who gave so freely of their time in order that we might better understand their situation. Most of the patients interviewed were at one time or other patients at the Alcoholism and Addiction Unit of the North West Metropolitan Regional Hospital Board at St. Bernard's Hospital, and we wish to thank the St. Bernard's Hospital Management Committee for their permission to carry out this research—although, of course, they are in no way responsible for any of the views expressed here. It is our hope that this volume will provide a better understanding of the addict and the pressures both internally and externally under which he operates.

M.M.G.
D.J.P.
D.G.G.
D.R.H.

1967

Contents

1 The Drug Age

Man's relationship to drugs is a long one; according to archae-
ologists and anthropologists, drugs have been used by man
before recorded history. They have been used for medicinal,
religious, pleasurable, and social purposes. Sometimes drugs
have been praised and, at other times, condemned by societies
throughout history. One drug, such as mescaline, may be highly
exalted by one society and, at the same time, prohibited by
another; or, another drug (for example, cannabis), may be
widely used and sought by one segment of a community and
frowned upon by another part of it. Over time a community's
attitude toward a drug may reverse itself; opiates were legally
accepted prior to World War I in the United States and were
prohibited after that point in time. The current drug problem
confronting Great Britain, the United States, and other countries is not a new phenomenon, although it is more complex
than previously.

Part of this increased complexity is related to the great
scientific advances in the field of pharmacology in the last fifty
years. Today we have at our disposal drugs that literally cover
the whole spectrum of a human behaviour. Besides 'The Pill',
we have pills to sedate us when we are nervous, excite us when
we are dull, slim us when we are fat, fatten us when we are
thin, wake us when we are sleepy, put us to sleep when we
are awake, cure us when we are sick, and make us sick
when we are well. Drugs can enhance our ability to function
or they can carry our mind out of the realm of reality into
loneliness.

It is, however, important to keep a proper perspective on
drugs which both solve and create problems. One has only to
think of such miracle drugs as penicillin to realize the benefits
brought to the treatment of illness. Given the sophistication of
drugs and their positive uses, they have achieved a high level
of acceptance by the general population in most countries.
Yet, any drug can be misused with negative consequences to

the individual and the society. Fortunately there are few drugs which are consistently misused.

In this chapter we will discuss most of the drugs that are related to the problem in Great Britain and the United States and which a considerable number of people misuse. We will also present a brief discussion of the problems related to drug terminology.

DRUG TERMINOLOGY

At this point, we are confronted with a thorny problem which all students of drugs face, namely, 'What is addiction?' There is much disagreement among authorities as to what actually constitutes addiction and, as a result, which drugs are addictive. One noted pharmacologist has stated:

'The true status of our knowledge regarding drug addiction is now as it has always been, i.e., a mystery. Much is known of the pharmacology of these agents but the exact mechanisms of addiction, and even analgesia, continue to be elusive.'[2]

One reason addiction continues to mystify is related to the multi-dimensional character of the phenomenon. Like alcoholism, drug addiction is typically the result of many interacting factors. It is not just the effect of the drug on the person, but the social-psychological state of the individual is crucial, i.e. how in his particular environment he reacts to the drug.

Since there are many different addictive drugs and many factors influence a person's becoming addicted, it is difficult to discover any direct cause-effect relationship for addiction. Thus, it is not sufficient to state that the reason a person is addicted is that he took excessive amounts of a certain drug. One must also consider the drug in question, the laws regarding it, the society's attitude toward the chemical agent (which is not always reflected in the laws), the individual's attitude toward it, and the physical and psychological make-up of the individual. Stated differently, knowledge of the drug *per se* is necessary for understanding addiction, but it is not sufficient for a full comprehension of the pathology.

There are four terms frequently used in the drug research literature which have relevance for this book. These are: *addiction, habituation, dependence,* and *abuse.* Unfortunately these terms frequently overlap in meaning and there are disagreements about their precise definitions. We shall now discuss each of these terms, taking into consideration their past and current usage.

ADDICTION

There are three properties which a drug must have before it **is** considered addictive; it must produce tolerance, abstinence (withdrawal) symptoms and craving. Tolerance means that the drug must be taken in progressively larger doses in order to achieve the desired result. Simplified, tolerance develops as follows: if a person begins to take daily 1 grain of drug A, he finds that at the end of several weeks the drug no longer affects him in the same manner. He then increases his dosage to 2 grains daily. Then, after a month or so, the person again realizes that drug A no longer produces the desired effect. He therefore increases his daily dosage to 3 grains, and so on.

If the person is suddenly prevented from taking any more of drug A, he experiences an abstinence syndrome. These symptoms vary from one drug to another and depend on the amount of drugs being taken. The abstinence syndrome is characterized by physical illness symptoms such as stomach cramps, diarrhoea, and irritability.

The person taking drug A will develop a craving for the drug which is due not only to the physical effects which the drug has on his body but also to the fact that he fears the abstinence syndrome. Too, he may develop a psychological craving which is not fully understood. Typically, many addicts who have been successfully withdrawn from a drug develop a strong desire to begin taking the drug again. This is one of several reasons why the relapse rate after treatment for addicts is extremely high.

HABITUATION

There are many habit-forming agents to which most of us succumb in various degrees, such as the use of coffee, tea, and chocolate. Of course, tobacco is also habit forming and is now considered by most medical authorities to be a health hazard. Also, some drugs are habit forming. Simply stated, all addictive drugs are habit forming, but not all habit-forming drugs are pharmacologically addictive. Habituation is primarily mental or psychological as a physical abstinence syndrome does not develop when the habit-forming agent is suddenly withdrawn from the individual. For example, a person may daily smoke a pack of cigarettes without developing tolerance and when they are withdrawn he does not develop an abstinence syndrome from not having tobacco. However, not all habit-forming drugs have the same characteristics as tobacco. There are habituating drugs, such as certain amphetamines, where tolerance does develop but there is no abstinence syndrome. In summary, habituation may consist of tolerance and craving (primarily psychological), but it is never followed by an abstinence syndrome.

DEPENDENCE

In 1964, the World Health Organization released a report[4] which, in effect, combined addiction and habituation under one term—dependence. The WHO Expert Committee on Addiction felt there existed much confusion between the terms addiction and habituation, and as a consequence, the classification of a drug as addictive or habit-forming was difficult. This Committee suggested that each type of drug should be described by its particular type of dependence, e.g. 'drug dependence of amphetamine type'. The WHO Committee's substitution of 'dependence' for the terms addiction and habituation is an attempt to clarify drug terminology. Only further basic research in the area of pharmacology, sociology, and psychology in reference to drugs and behaviour will solve the problems of classification and terminology.

ABUSE OR MISUSE

Almost all drugs have been produced for medical, clinical, or other scientific reasons and their consumption is generally controlled by law. Persons who take drugs illegally and/or for some purpose other than that for which the drug was commonly designed or in a manner other than prescribed by the doctor are said to be abusing the drug. It should be indicated that people who are dependent on drugs are also usually abusing them. However, there are some people who take drugs but never become dependent upon them. Some individuals whose case histories are presented in this book have frequently experimented with many drugs. They have taken some drugs periodically for a few months and then have discontinued them. Persons who use drugs for other than the generally accepted reasons or who take them illegally but are not dependent on the drug will be defined as drug abusers or misusers.

'PROBLEM DRUGS'

We shall now discuss some of the more 'problematic' drugs which currently compose the British drug abuse scene. In late chapters, through case histories chiefly, the social implications of drug dependence and abuse will be presented. For now, a brief statement on each of these problematic drugs will suffice. For purposes of discussion they are divided into five categories. These are: (1) cannabis; (2) amphetamines; (3) barbiturates; (4) opiates, synthetic opiates, and cocaine; and (5) hallucinogens.

CANNABIS

Marijuana, charas, hemp, hashish, bhang, pot, tea, and weed are just a few of the terms used throughout the world to describe products of the female plant *Cannabis sativa* (or Indian hemp). Cannabis has been used for medicinal, social, and pleasurable purposes for thousands of years, rivalling opium in its history. The drug was mentioned in a Chinese pharmacy book written in 2737 B.C.[3] It was popular with Indian philosophers and was widely used by Arabs at the time of the Crusades.

The plant's popularity has not diminished in the Middle East and India; currently cannabis is enjoying wide acceptance in Western countries despite national and international efforts to suppress its use. Also, cannabis's approbation in Great Britain is entirely the result of non-medical purposes, for it is no longer used as a medicine.

In Britain, cannabis is commonly called pot, marijuana, charge, weed, hashish or hash, and grass. It is almost always smoked in the form of a cigarette which is referred to as a smoke, joint or reefer. Occasionally, cannabis is smoked with opium; this mixture is termed charas. Cannabis varies greatly in its potency which correlates with the growing conditions to which the plant is subjected. The best grade of cannabis is grown in semi-arid regions. Also, two basic types of cannabis are smuggled into Britain. (Cannabis will grow in the United Kingdom, but its quality is quite poor.) There is the regular cannabis which consists of the pulverized leaves and stems of the plant. Then there is the more powerful type which is made up largely of dried resin from the flower of the plant; this type of cannabis is hash or hashish.

The effect cannabis has on individuals varies greatly. This variance can partly be explained by the different grades of cannabis. However, it has also been suggested that persons learn what to expect from the drug before they actually take it.[1] Thus, if someone is advised that pot will help him appreciate the 'true' meaning of a painting, the painting will take on new and exciting dimensions for the pot smoker. How much the pharmacology of the drug has to do with the experience is difficult to discern. Still there are several general effects that cannabis appears to have on most persons. Users talk of the drug's euphoric qualities which give them a sense of well-being, light-headedness, and pleasant experiences in perceiving things.

Cannabis is not physically addictive. Although habituation has been reported in the Middle East it is not very common to find someone habituated to the drug in Western countries, but we have two cases of this type reported in this book (pp. 56, 73). Users frequently compare it favourably to alcohol, saying it is less dangerous, results in a better form of intoxication, and does not have the unpleasant after-effects frequently associated with alcohol. Among its advocates, cannabis is considered a social drug like alcohol, only not as harmful as the latter, they believe. Yet, cannabis is illegal. It has been accused of leading persons to using dangerous drugs, such as heroin. True, some persons who take cannabis later become dependent upon other drugs; however, many users of cannabis never progress to taking dangerous drugs. In short, it is incorrect to state that there exists a direct causal relationship between taking cannabis and addictive drugs.

As a result of the illegality of cannabis, persons who use it frequently associate with others illicitly taking other drugs, and vice versa. The cannabis smoker may frequently come into contact with other drug users, and because of this he is more likely to become dependent upon some other drug than is someone from the general public under such circumstances.

6

This would not be due to any inherent properties of cannabis; rather, the dependence would be the result of social milieu associated with cannabis (which is caused in no small part by its illegality) and the socio-psychological make-up of the individual.

AMPHETAMINES

Amphetamine or Benzedrine was developed during the late 1920's. Since then, many other 'amphetamines' have been developed; chemical derivatives of Benzedrine such as Dexedrine, Methedrine, Durophet, and the amphetamine-like product Preludin. These drugs stimulate the central nervous system and were widely used medically to combat fatigue, depression, and obesity. Amphetamines, besides stimulating the individual, also produce euphoria to a limited extent and, in general, give the user a sense of well-being. The public frequently refers to these drugs as 'pep pills'.

Amphetamines are habit forming; in the past most cases of dependence were found among middle-aged housewives who frequently had the drug prescribed to them by doctors in connection with weight reduction. More recently, amphetamine dependence is seen among teenagers who obtained the drug illegally in order to stay awake over week-ends. Some youth use it as an alternative to alcohol, i.e. as a means to facilitate social interaction. Undoubtedly the majority of youth who use amphetamines are only misusers and never become dependent upon the substance. For those who do become dependent, many exhibit the following symptoms: impairment of psychomotor function, insomnia, anorexia, paranoia, general restlessness, psycho-social deterioration and a very unpleasant withdrawal ('come down') syndrome (depression).

Besides amphetamines, there are also amphetamine-barbiturate combinations. The most popular is Drinamyl, better known among youth as 'Purple Hearts' or 'French Blues'. This drug has more or less the same effect as a pure amphetamine, but the barbiturate element tends to keep the user from becoming too restless and excited; also the effect of the drug does not wear off as abruptly as an amphetamine when the dosage is discontinued.

BARBITURATES

Derived from barbituric acid, barbiturates were first developed in the latter part of the nineteenth century and became popular in the early 1900's. Today they are extensively used in Western countries. This drug acts on the central nervous system by calming and, if used in sufficient strength, sedating the individual. Thus, these pills are sometimes referred to as 'sleepers'. Typically, barbiturates are prescribed for insomnia and nervousness, and to a lesser degree are used as an anaesthetic. Some common barbiturates are Nembutal, Amytal, and Seconal. Unfortunately, they are pharmacologically addictive if taken excessively over a period of time.

Before 1960, barbiturate dependence was typically a condition of middle-aged persons, especially females, and some alcoholics. It should be emphasized that alcohol and barbiturates are a dangerous combination since both are depressants and used together can even lead to accidental death. More recently, barbiturate dependence has been noted among youngsters, though they usually employ barbiturates in combination with other drugs. Occasionally a doctor prescribes a barbiturate to someone using cocaine or amphetamines. The latter two excite and activate a person to such a degree that relaxing and sleeping are difficult; therefore, barbiturates are used to combat these symptoms of agitation. Some of the symptoms of barbiturate-dependence state are the inability to coordinate to voluntary body movements, to control emotions and to think normally. Barbiturates have a cross-tolerance, i.e. one barbiturate can be substituted for another.

OPIATES, SYNTHETIC OPIATES, AND COCAINE

For over 4,000 years man has cultivated opium poppies in Asia for the drug opium which has been eaten, smoked, and drunk in solutions. Although nowadays in Britain opium use is not found often, it is sometimes used for smoking. More important today are the opiates derived from opium. Three of the best known ones are morphine, heroin, and codeine. Besides opiates, there have been many synthetic opiates developed such as methadone and pethidine. Medically these drugs have proved valuable, especially as analgesics. They depress the central nervous system and, by so doing, make the person unaware of his pain. They also have a mild euphoric effect which gives the individual a feeling of complacent well-being.

All opiates and synthetic opiates are pharmacologically addictive. Persons becoming dependent do not suffer serious symptoms directly from the drugs. They frequently become constipated and are drowsy. The most serious effects are indirectly associated with the drug in that addicts typically become totally preoccupied with it and lose interest in sex, work, food, and clothes. This disinterest, of course, has a negative effect on their health in that they frequently develop infections from unsterile injections (practically all addicts inject their drugs intramuscularly or intravenously). These drugs have a cross-tolerance so that one opiate can be substituted for another.

Cocaine is not an opiate, nor is it pharmacologically addictive. It is included in this section because it is frequently taken in combination with the opiates in Great Britain.

Cocaine is derived from the coca plant. South American Indians have chewed coca leaves throughout their recorded history for their stimulating effect. Cocaine is more powerful than coca, but opiate addicts use it primarily for the same reasons as the Indians. Opiates sedate the person and make him listless; cocaine counteracts the depressing effect of opiates and gives the users more 'life'. Also, cocaine offers a bigger 'kick' or 'buzz' (although fleeting) as a result of its being a relatively powerful stimulant.

Individuals can develop a cocaine habit and a tolerance for the drug. There is, however, no physical abstinence syndrome.

HALLUCINOGENS

The three principal drugs in this group are mescaline, psilocybin, and lysergic acid diethylamide (LSD 25 or LSD). These drugs are also designated as phantastica, psychedelic, and psychotomimetic drugs. The variety of descriptive terms indicates the numerous attitudes toward these drugs and our limited knowledge of them. Hallucinogenic, of course, means producing hallucinations, yet there is some doubt about whether the drugs produce hallucinations or simply distort perception. To correct this confusion, some experts prefer giving these drugs the equally uncertain term, phantastica, which means falling somewhere between hallucinations and illusions. An even more obscure title, at least for persons who have not taken the drug, is psychedelic. This term (mind-opening or mind-manifesting) refers to that quality of these drugs which allows the person to expand his 'consciousness'.

The psychedelic experience or 'trip' allows the user to become 'aware of things he did not know existed' and to remember his very early childhood. Lastly, is the term psychotomimetic (mimic psychosis).

The above terms have been brought about by the researchers' inability to discover exactly how this group of drugs (which we have called 'hallucinogens') acts on the brain. As a result, the scientists have described the drug by its manifestations, i.e. how people overtly react to it.

Unfortunately, people react in different ways which are related not only to the amount and frequency of dosage, but to environmental variables. For example, individuals who initially take a hallucinogen under the direction of a 'guide' (a person who has experience with the drug) are led and guided throughout their 'trip'. The guide tells the initiate what to expect, how to react, and, on the whole, assists him throughout his drug experience. As a result, the journey will vary from one guide to another. Also, persons who take hallucinogens on their own will experience different effects depending in part on their surroundings and personality. To a lesser extent, the above analysis holds true for the other drugs we have discussed But, as we shall now document, hallucinogens are extremely powerful and affect users in a way that can justly be called bizarre.

LSD, psilocybin, and mescaline all have similar effects, although LSD is, by far, the most powerful of the three. It is a synthetic drug discovered in 1943. Although realizing this was a most unusual and powerful drug, scientists were at somewhat of a loss to find a use for LSD. Contrastingly, Indians had been using psilocybin (found in certain Mexican mushrooms) and mescaline (found in the peyote cactus indigenous to the southwestern part of the United States and northern Mexico) for centuries, mainly in religious ceremonies. (Psilocybin and mescaline can now be produced synthetically.) Soon these hallucinogens were being used in clinical experiments and as a therapeutic aid. It has been reported to have been used for treating psychiatric diseases, alcoholism, and rehabilitating criminals. The common factor in all these therapies seems to be that the patients 'gain a greater insight of themselves and the world', and thus may be better equipped to cope with their problems. Critics point out that these studies never 'prove' that hallucinogens are beneficial—that the researchers never develop rigid control experiments which would truly test the efficacy of the drug.

Today what is creating great concern in Western society is the illicit use of hallucinogens. It is one thing to give an hallucinogen in a clinical setting, quite another to take the drug in a layman's flat. These powerful drugs alter the mind of the user in some manner which produces strange, sometimes beautiful, at other times horrible, hallucinations or illusions. In most cases, users suffer few after-effects, nor do they become pharmacologically addicted. But more serious are the tragic consequences sometimes produced through the illicit use of these drugs to engender a hallucinogen 'trip'. People have attempted to fly out of windows and stop trains or cars under the influence of these drugs. It may be that the drug was not the cause of the accidents; it is possible that the persons were mentally unbalanced before taking the drug, or perhaps the drug acted as a catalyst by exaggerating some minor psychological defect. Until we know more about this class of drug, its use should be confined to experimental clinics. Unfortunately, this is impossible, for there is already a black market for them in Great Britain and the United States.

REFERENCES

1. Becker, H. (1953) Becoming a Marihuana User. *Amer. J. Sociol.,* **59**, 235–42.
2. Sherrod, T. M. (1966) The Pharmacology and Physiology of Drug Addiction. *Drug Addiction : Illinois med. J.,* October, **130**, 453.
3. Taylor, D. (1963) *Narcotics : Nature's Dangerous Gifts?* Dell, New York, p. 12.
4. WHO Expert Committee on Addiction Producing Drugs (1964) *Wld. Hlth Org. techn. Rep. Ser.* No. 273.

2 The British Drug Scene*

During the summer of 1965, at the time the Second Brain Commission Report was being prepared, a study of British drug addicts and abusers was conducted in the London Metropolitan area. We interviewed as many drug addicts as possible during a limited period, drawing our sample from as wide a base as possible. Addicts were reached through six sources. These were: (1) the Addiction Unit of a large psychiatric hospital; (2) a specialized nursing home treating female alcoholics and addicts; (3) a prison; (4) the outpatient clinic of a general hospital; (5) a specialized outpatient clinic for addicts; and (6) a flat frequented by drug addicts.

Information and opinions were also collected from medical and administrative personnel dealing with drugs and addicts. The interviews were informal and were used to elicit information about the addicts' attitudes to and relationship with existing avenues of treatment and control. Most subjects were interviewed once, and the majority of interviews were recorded on tapes. Twenty-six addicts were interviewed and, of these, 16 were addicted to heroin and cocaine, and 10 to other drugs of dependence.

This chapter is presented in three major sections which are: (1) a summary of the British system of drug control; (2) a demographic portrait of the drug addict and abuser; and (3) the British system and the drug subculture.

THE BRITISH SYSTEM OF DRUG CONTROL

The so-called British system of control is old, and has remained essentially unchanged since 1926. In that year a committee of medical men forming the Rolleston Committee interpreted the Dangerous Drugs Law to mean that a drug

* Adapted from D. Gillespie, M. M. Glatt, D. R. Hills, and D. J. Pittman (1967) Drug Dependence and Abuse in England. *Brit. J. Addict.* **62**, 155–170.

addict is a sick person, and should be allowed drugs when 'the patient while capable of leading a useful and relatively normal life when a certain minimum dose is regularly administered becomes incapable of this when the drug is entirely discontinued'. It is thus evident that the doctor plays a crucial role in the interpretation of the system.

Contrary to popular belief, there is no register of addicts at the Home Office (see Chapter 9), but a record of 'addicts known to the Home Office' is kept, and this is compiled by referring to the records of chemist shops and from information volunteered by doctors treating addicts. This list of known addicts is kept on an annual basis, and includes only the names of those persons who have received drugs in any given year. This contrasts with the system employed in the United States where the Federal Bureau of Narcotics keeps a person's name listed as an addict for five years, even though it is not known whether he has taken drugs or not during that period. Ostensibly the British system seems very simple; indeed Lindesmith has stated:

'The British program with respect to addicts is in reality absurdly simple, and almost impossible to misunderstand. The addict simply goes to a doctor, confides in him, and is taken care of by the doctor. The latter is under a professional obligation to attempt to cure the addict, but there is no provision for forced cures, and the user must therefore be *persuaded* to submit himself to a hospital for withdrawal of the drug.'[7]

However, the Government's awareness of a growing illicit traffic in dangerous drugs, especially amphetamines, led to the enactment of the Drugs (Prevention of Misuse) Act in 1964 and later in 1965 The Dangerous Drug Act. Basically, these statutes give greater powers to the police to search, seize, and prosecute drug abusers, particularly for illegal importation and possession of dangerous drugs.

In this connection we would like to draw attention to three significant changes in conviction trends for drug offences. First, between 1961 and 1962 the number of convictions for cannabis violations, particularly for possession, increased by over 100%—from 288 to 588 cases. Second, between 1963 and 1964 convictions involving manufactured drugs, chiefly heroin and cocaine, increased by approximately 60%—from 63 to 101 cases. Third, in 1966 the largest number of convictions ever recorded in Great Britain involving dangerous drugs occurred and this was more than a 50% increase over the previous year—from 767 to 1,174 cases. While there are marked limitations to using such data based on convictions as the only evidence for the increasing drug problem, they do highlight, when taken in connection with the increasing number of known drug addicts, the seriousness of the drug situation in Great Britain.

DEMOGRAPHIC PORTRAIT OF THE DRUG ADDICT AND ABUSER

In 1962 *Narcotic Addiction in Britain and America: The Impact of Public Policy*,[10] by Edwin Schur, an American lawyer and sociologist, was published. This book is the only contemporary study available on British addiction which employs empirical data, and for this reason is extremely important. In his study, Schur utilizes, among others, 11 areas of analysis, which are: (1) occupation, (2) social class, (3) age, (4) sex, (5) marriage, (6) sex life, (7) proselytism, (8) occupational adjustment, (9) criminality, (10) nationality, and (11) the addict subculture. These areas will be related to our material in the course of this chapter.

OCCUPATION

Schur states that: 'All available evidence supports the contention that a large proportion of British addicts is found in medical and related occupations'.[9] He found that of 73 addicts admitted to a large mental hospital, 54 (74%) were in 'medical or allied occupations'. Schur contends that this sample may well not be 'fully representative of British addicts generally'. [9] It is possible, for example, that many doctors prefer treatment at a specific hospital, especially if this hospital primarily treats middle-class addicts. Schur does not identify the hospital, but it is known that it was in the London area. Schur's hospital sample was not typical, for the percentage of addicts in the medical or related professions known to the Home Office during this period was always under 25% (Table 1).

Reference to a 1964 study of Hewetson and Ollendorf[4] who investigated a sample of 100 addicts gives the following distribution: 12 jazz musicians, 12 casual labourers, 6 prostitutes, 4 seamen, 3 post-graduates, 2 industrial chemists and

Table 1. Medical personnel addicts known to the Home Office

	Years								
	1951	1954	1957	1959	1963	1964	1965	1966	1967
Total number of addicts	301	317	359	454	635	753	927	1,349	1,729
Total number of addicts in medical or allied occupations	77	72	88	68	56	58	45	54	56
Per cent of total addicts in medical or allied occupations	25	23	24	15	9	8	5	4	3

2 nurses. The remaining 59 addicts were not classified, but showed a 'great number of semi-skilled professional men and women'.

No doubt, relative to other professions, medical personnel are disproportionately over-represented in the addict population. The literature on drug dependence suggests this to be true in most countries. However, what is more important to the overall phenomenon of drug addiction is the percentage of the total drug addict population made up by medical personnel. Table 1 shows the percentage of addicts in medical or allied occupations for the total number of addicts known to the Home Office. In recent years this proportion has decreased as the total number of addicts increased. There are two possible explanations for this tendency. First, it is possible that the actual number of medical personnel addicts is decreasing or, second, that the number has remained constant, but that an increasing number are not known to the Home Office. It is true that the number of medical personnel has been consistently small, and one must take care not to exaggerate the importance of a loss or gain of 20 or 30 in their number. The use of this particular occupational group as an index of change in the larger addict population may prove useful. It would seem that Schur was using this occupational group to draw an alternative conclusion, namely, that the addict population was stable. Referring to opinion in America, Winick[12] has suggested that the American doctor addicts fear the stigma attached to them as a result of their addiction. They feel above the common 'street addict' and react negatively when confronted with one of them. It is also true that awareness of drug dependency on the part of society has grown in recent years. Simultaneously, a negative attitude towards drug addiction has become apparent. It could be argued that fewer medical personnel become addicts because they fear a negative label from society. However, a more plausible explanation would be that British medical personnel still become addicts at the same rate, but are more secretive as a result of the negative attitudes surrounding them.

SOCIAL CLASS

On the basis of 'incomplete' and 'general'[9] information from pharmacists and medical specialists, Schur suggests that British drug addicts typically come from the middle or upper-middle classes. A study of drug addicts treated at St. Bernard's Hospital Unit between 1959 and 1965 shows that the majority did not come from these classes. For example, in 1965 on the basis of the Registrar General's Classification, the 16 heroin and cocaine addicts interviewed for this part of the study were distributed as follows: (social) Class I—0; Class II—2; Class III—9; Class IV and V—5.*

A similar distribution was found in the 100 drug addicts investigated by Hewetson and Ollendorf.[4] This sample, broken down similarly, gives the following distribution: (social) Class I—2; Class II—23; Class III—52; and Class IV and V—23. A distribution based on educational attainment of this sample shows that 3 had university education, 29 matriculation, 48 had no examination but had completed the statutory course leaving at age 14 or 15, and 20 were near illiteracy.

Schur contrasts the lack of working-class addicts with the prominence of addiction found in the lower American social classes. He quotes Ausubel who says, 'The disproportionate number of addicts who originate in the lower class can undoubtedly be attributed to the greater availability of drugs in slum areas'.[10] This does not explain why there is a greater availability in the lower class and not in the middle and upper

* I. Professional, etc. II. Intermediate. III. Skilled occupation. IV: Partly skilled. V. Unskilled.

classes. There must be some other factor to explain why drug
pedlars find a ready market at the lower end of the social scale
in the United States. Applying this reasoning to the situation
in England, one would have expected that Schur would have
found an equal distribution of drug addiction throughout the
social classes since each has equal access to drugs. It would
seem that the distribution in England over the past few years
involves individuals from a much wider social background.
They certainly include a large number of working-class youth
today, quite different from Schur's description.

AGE

Again basing the conclusion on information supplied by pharmacists and medical practitioners treating addicts, Schur
states 'that most British addicts are over 30 years of age'.[9] He
further states:

'Clearly the age of addicts is related to the differential exposure to
drugs of various class and occupational groups. If many or most
British addicts are doctors (and this would strongly suggest professional access to drugs as a major circumstance in the introduction
to drug use), it can easily be seen why the onset of addiction typically
would not occur before the age of thirty.'[9]

The official records of the Home Office in 1965 begin to
question Schur's contention that most addicts are over 30 years
of age—as Table 2 shows. Unfortunately, the age category
20–34 is too wide to allow one to determine the number of
addicts in their twenties. The figures do show quite dramatically
that an increasing number of younger addicts are becoming
known to the Home Office. The mean age of the 16 heroin and
cocaine addicts interviewed in this survey was 26·7 years, and
of addicts admitted to St. Bernard's Hospital Addiction Unit
between 1959 and 1965 the mean age of males was 22·9 years,
11 of this group being 20 years old or under. Of 9 female addicts
seen, 4 were 20 or under, and the group had a mean age of 23
years. The growing number of young addicts, that is to say,
those in their late teens or early twenties, in England seems to
be a very recent phenomenon, and at the time of Schur's research there were probably few addicts under 30 years of age.
This shift in age distribution of the addict population is very
important.

Table 2. Age of drug addicts known to the Home Office

Ages	Years							
	1959	1960	1962	1963	1964	1965	1966	1967
Under 20	—	1	3	17	40	145	329	395
20–34	50	62	132	184	257	347	558	906
35–49	92	91	107	128	138	134	162	142
50 and over	278	267	274	298	311	291	286	279
Unknown	34	16	16	8	7	10	14	7
Total	454	437	532	635	753	927	1,349	1,729

SEX

Schur's contention is that 'the differing legal definitions of addiction—in the U.S. as a crime, in Britain as a disease—have in themselves affected the sex ratios for addiction', i.e. 'the high proportion of female addicts in Great Britain'.[10] Recent data from the Home Office no longer support this conjecture. Specifically, the sex distribution of the new cases of heroin addiction recorded from 1960–1964 for British subjects report 220 male cases (70%) and only 81 female cases. Since the largest group of additional addicts reported in Great Britain since 1961 have been heroin users, the sex distribution will become even more predominantly male. In 1965, of all addicts known to the Home Office, 558 (60%) of them were males.

MARRIAGE AND SEXUAL ACTIVITY

The findings of Schur and others regarding marriage and sexual activity were confirmed. The psychological and physiological effects of narcotics make a normal sex life impossible for most addicts; both male and female addicts report loss of sexual desire, and in males impotence is commonly found. Of the 100 addicts studied by Hewetson and Ollendorff,[4] 22 were married (including 4 couples where both partners were addicts), 7 were separated or divorced, and 71 were single. Of the 16 heroin and cocaine addicts interviewed at St. Bernard's Hospital, 4 were married, 1 was divorced, 1 was widowed, and 10 were single.

THE BRITISH SYSTEM AND THE DRUG SUBCULTURE

We shall now consider attitudes of addicts to the 'British system', and to each other. The emergence of several types of subcultures will be discussed. Speaking of drug addiction in England in 1963, Schur says:

'Britain has fairly well prevented addiction from spreading to other persons typically believed to be susceptible to addiction. It can hardly be maintained that there is a paucity of such persons in Britain. The well recognised connection between supply and demand mechanisms, and underworld operations lies at the heart of the matter. This writer knows of no evidence, or common sense argument, refuting the assertion that low cost and legal provision of drugs (as in Britain) inevitably curtails illicit traffic.'[9]

This statement implies that there does not exist a drug problem in England of the same magnitude as found in the United States because there is no drug underworld. Furthermore, there is no illicit drug traffic because there is no market, and finally there is no market because of the British system.

As Schur recognizes, historically England has never experienced a drug addiction problem comparable to that found in the United States. There, before the Harrison Act of 1914, any person could buy narcotics from his local 'drug store'. People were quite frequently unaware of their addiction, but marvelled at the soothing powers of certain brands of patent medicines. Just how much of a 'problem' drug addicts constituted during the early 1900's in the United States is uncertain. It was estimated, however, that there were 200,000 addicts at this time. Using the Harrison Act (which was initially designed as a Revenue Law for taxing narcotics), courts and police began suppressing the use of narcotic drugs. By the early 1920's the United States had an extensive underworld trafficking in narcotics. Sequentially then, the United States underworld developed in the following manner:

1. There existed a large number of individuals using a substance.
2. Another group of individuals for various reasons viewed the consumption of this substance as undesirable, and this group placed sanctions on the consumers and attempted to stop trafficking in the substance.

3. The market still existed for this substance, but legal sources were nonexistent.
4. A third group of individuals sold the substance through illegal channels for large profits. This would be a typical prototype for an underworld marketing process, and was repeated during American Prohibition (1920–1933).

Central to Schur's thesis is the concept that the underworld plays a crucial role in the development of drug addiction, particularly among the lower classes; yet referring to the American pattern outlined above we can see that this is not the case. It would seem that England has never had a black market or underworld centred upon drugs simply because there has never been a market. Yet Schur states that there is no market due to the British drug policy, i.e. addicts do not have to turn to the underworld since they are able to get drugs legally, cheaply, and of good quality. He also states that no black market exists because there is no underworld. It must be remembered that Britain has never had a large number of addicts or an underworld of the proportions found in the United States. Thus it would be fair to say that the British system has never been tested, and that the system was not developed to prevent the growth of addiction or a drug-oriented underworld.

The sudden increase in numbers of drug addicts in recent years has put the British system to a test, and this testing continues gaining in intensity as time goes by. In 1959, there were 454 drug addicts known to the Home Office; this figure grew to 927 in 1965, an increase of over 100%. Perhaps more important is the fact that there were only 98 non-therapeutic addicts in 1959, but 372 in 1964, an increase of 279%. In 1965 there were 580 addicts of non-therapeutic origin.

Since the British policy has remained essentially unchanged since the 1920's, and there is still no organized underworld dealing with narcotics, there must be some other explanation for this growth. Before discussing why, let us consider how these new individuals became addicted.

THE SPREAD OF ADDICTION: PUSHING AND 'REGISTRATION'

Schur, quoting Lindesmith, believes 'There is little or no economic incentive to spread the habit to others'.[9] He goes on to say that 'Not only can the British addict avoid personal involvement in the sale of illicit drugs, but actually there is very little illicit trafficking at all, on anyone's part'.[9]

Concerning the question of the lack of 'economic incentive', Schur points out that 'Even British addicts appear to have considerable job difficulties', and that 'Most addicts probably will remain social liabilities of sorts'.[9] Thus Schur's data and our own show that British addicts characteristically cannot undertake a productive role in society.

The actual buying of drugs on National Health Service prescriptions places no economic strain on the addict. Yet, the addict like everyone else must have food, shelter, and clothing. One way in which he earns money for essentials is by selling drugs to other addicts. Of the 16 heroin and cocaine addicts interviewed, all reluctantly admitted selling drugs illegally. The typical initial answer to the question if they had ever sold drugs was a flat 'no'. However, on closer questioning they would admit to selling drugs; a typical reply was 'Yes, I pushed it, but I never recommend it for anything. If a guy wants it, he will get it, what the hell, man.' This same addict freely admitted to 'pushing marijuana', saying, 'I pushed some weed, but "charge" don't hurt nobody'.

Two questions arise from the foregoing; firstly, why should anyone want to buy drugs illegally at fairly high prices (from 20s per grain) when they can get drugs from a doctor on prescription? and secondly, where do the addicts get the drugs they sell?

The first question is fairly easily answered, and has been discussed by Lemert,[6] Goffman,[3] and Schur.[10] Typical comments from addict regarding registration are given below:

'I didn't want to register. Once you're registered it goes in to the Home Office. It's with you the rest of your life. I didn't want to get hooked on heroin; once you're registered, you're hooked. It's too depressing when you're hooked, besides, a girl looks terrible on heroin.'

Thus, addicts do not want to look upon themselves or others to look upon them as drug addicts (see Chapter 9); this suggests that addicts themselves view addiction as an undesirable condition and wish to delay any formal process which would label them as addicts. Implicit in the addicts' attitudes is an awareness that society views drug addiction negatively. To illustrate how addicts get drugs when they are not registered is explained in detail in the case studies. How addicts sometimes get drugs when they are registered (on a doctor's list) is illustrated by the following remark:

'The reason you get registered for more than you need is not just to sell, but once you get registered you're fixed for say 6 grains; well, over time your habit gets worse, and you need more, but the doctors don't take this into consideration. You just get the same amount so that, you know, in the beginning you say, I am taking 8 or 10 or something so that you have got months and months to play with.'

One interesting idea expressed by addicts is that they are not addicted until they become 'registered'. In effect, they say that they probably would not have been addicts if they had not 'registered'. This gives weight to the addicts' notion that 'once you're "registered", you're really hooked'. It is doubtful if many addicts are simply abusers when they become registered.

CRIMINALITY

Sometimes addicts are arrested for possession of drugs obtained illegally. A typical example was a 26-year-old male addict who had been convicted and sent to prison five times, and sent for 'cures' twenty-two times. His convictions were for altering dates on prescriptions, forging prescriptions, and for breaking and entering chemist shops. It would seem that the most common offence amongst the 'registered' addict population is altering prescriptions. Another addict when asked if it was difficult to get drugs illegally said, 'Not really. I mean, in this country if someone's sick he can find drugs. Say he is not due to pick up a "scrip" (prescription) for two hours or something, he can usually find someone.'

Sometimes the addict does have difficulty in getting drugs; for a 'registered' addict this takes place when he 'blows' or sells a prescription in one day that is supposed to last for, say, three days. One addict relates his experience when this happened to him:

'Well then you just shiver for a few days, you just have to go out and hustle and hustle the drug, borrow it. This is when things get difficult, you know, it all comes down black and thick.'

When asked if he ever went back to his G.P. with an explanation, he said, 'Oh yes, it doesn't matter what story you tell the doctor, they still know that you're short of the drug'. Although it would seem less typical, some addicts supplement their incomes by petty crimes. As one addict said:

'Invariably the addict doesn't have enough "bread" to make the scene. I mean, he's always hustling for money. Begging, stealing, I always stole little stuff like art books, car radios, you know, man, all junkies do this. You gotta live, man.'

Before examining the other side of the coin, the attitudes of British doctors and administrators towards addicts and addiction, let us summarize what we have said thus far. The number of addicts known to the Home Office has grown steadily since 1951, and since 1959 the number has increased even more rapidly. The figures quoted are those of addicts known to the Home Office, and one might suspect that there exists a large number not found in these records; for example, if addicts characteristically postpone what they term 'registration', then the new addicts would not be represented in the official figures and younger addicts would therefore be grossly under-represented.

This postponement of 'registration' by addicts suggests that they view themselves as deviants, and that they wish to delay going to the doctor for prescriptions and ultimately having their names on the Home Office records 'by which persons come to be defined as deviant by others'.[5] Furthermore, addicts who sell and obtain drugs illegally from one another do not consider themselves to be 'pushers'. Engaging in this illegal activity changes their role from a 'sick' person to that of a criminal. This secondary deviancy (a kind of pseudo-underworld or black market) is the result of the addicts' inability to function productively in society, and is an unanticipated consequence of the British system. As we have already pointed out, the British system was not designed to deal with either non-therapeutic addicts or with a relatively large number of addicts. It was devised to deal with the number and types of addicts found in England in the 1920's. The system then put into operation was intended to be dealt with exclusively by the medical profession. In the light of the current situation, it would not seem that under this system the British medical profession has felt able to accept this responsibility fully.

THE MEDICAL PROFESSION AND THE ADDICT

In 1959, Schur found that 13 doctors in the London area were the main source of drugs for London addicts, and since almost all addicts were concentrated in London, this would constitute the principal source of the drugs for the country as a whole. In 1965 the Home Office was of the opinion that there were still only about 13 doctors who regularly treated addicts even though there was an increase in their figures of 299 addicts during the period. In conversation, one government official said:

'Our addiction, until the last few years, has been mainly therapeutic. However, one could see the problem in the 50's, say around '55, and it has grown steadily since. I suppose the problem has always been there. Loopholes in our system have existed since the Dangerous Drugs Act; it is a very confusing situation.'

It is a confusing situation, and it is all too easy to condemn the medical profession for apparently not accepting responsibility for the addict. We have already seen that addicts frequently take advantage of the few doctors who do see addicts. Many doctors have experienced an addict pounding on their door at three in the morning begging for a prescription. On the other hand, a minority of doctors, for reasons unknown, appear to treat addicts apparently without taking any practical steps to cure them. Cases are known where addicts claim the doctors have actually encouraged them to continue with the habit. Below is the reply to the question, 'How long were you with Dr. X?'

'About a year, or something like that. A year, and then I got a cure. I stayed off it just a few months, and then I got registered with Dr. Y. After about three months this doctor sort of began asking me for money because I was a private patient.'

In 1965 The Second Report of the Interdepartmental Committee on Drug Addiction examined the question of doctors' attitudes towards the care of addicts. It stated:

'From the evidence before us, we have been led to the conclusion that the major source of supply has been the activity of very few doctors who have prescribed excessively for addicts. Thus we were informed that in 1962 one doctor alone prescribed almost 600,000 tablets of heroin (i.e. 6 kilogrammes) for addicts. The same doctor, on one occasion, prescribed 900 tablets of heroin (9 grammes) to one addict, and three days later, prescribed for the same patient

another 600 tablets (6 grammes) "to replace pills lost in an accident."
Further prescriptions of 720, i.e. 7·2 grammes, and 840, i.e. 8·4 grammes, of tablets followed later to the same patient. Two doctors each
issued a single prescription for 1000 tablets (i.e. 10 grammes).
These are only the more startling examples. We heard of other
instances of prescriptions for considerable, if less spectacular,
quantities of dangerous drugs over a long period of time. Supplies
on such a scale can easily provide a surplus that will attract new
recruits to the ranks of the addicts. The evidence further shows that
not more than six doctors have prescribed these very large amounts
of dangerous drugs for individual patients and these doctors have
acted within the law and according to their professional judgement.'[1]

Simply put, there are only a few doctors who are prepared to
treat addicts, and even fewer others who, although within their
legal rights, do, in view of the Brain Commission, nothing to
help the situation. It might be argued that were there sufficient
doctors sympathetic towards the treatment of addicts, then
addicts would not need to visit the very small minority of
doctors referred to in the Second Brain Commission Report.
But this line of thought has a basic flaw, for many addicts
would continue to go to the doctor who enabled them to continue the habit rather than go to the doctor who would attempt
withdrawal and cure.

There are addiction units in hospitals in England where
addicts can be withdrawn from drugs fairly easily, but addicts
themselves have no strong motivation for an enduring cure with
the system as it is. Dependence is perhaps functional for most
addicts (it serves their personal and social needs), and addiction—in their subculture—is perhaps a sign of status as was
suggested in Finestone's[2] study. It is highly unlikely that
British doctors will suddenly unite in a conscientious effort to
help the addicts. In general, addicts have a very poor prognosis,
and basic to the ideology of most doctors is that they should
attempt to cure their patients. This of course means that the
doctor must first accept the idea that drug addiction is a disease and treatable in general practice. It would seem that this
idea is not yet accepted by many British doctors. The fact that
only 13 doctors make a practice of treating addicts supports
this opinion.

The first task of a doctor would be to show the addict why he
should stop taking drugs. This is not an easy task in view of
addicts' beliefs about the magical powers of drugs in meeting
their personal and social problems. For the few doctors in

general practice who may truly desire to treat and help addicts there are factors which would put off the most resolute. As Hewetson and Ollendorf[4] have explained:

'The work involved in serving the addict as part of a general practitioner's work is so great that it becomes clear that not only is there a disinclination on the part of the practitioner to serve this group of people on account of the many difficulties and legal complications which are a consequence of the Dangerous Drug Act, but clearly the work involved is so great that normally the general practitioner in a busy practice would be unable to cope with it all.'[4]

There has been an increase in the number of addicts known to the Home Office during the last six years. These official figures probably under-represent young addicts. This increase cannot be explained, as Schur suggests, by the presence of an underworld operation or the lack of a liberal policy towards drug addiction. Also, the increase in addicts has compounded the inherent flaws in the British system. Namely, the system was not designed for a large number of addicts and non-therapeutic addicts; it places the responsibility of addiction on the shoulders of the medical profession alone without the help of social agencies in a systematic after-care programme for addicts.

NATIONALITY AND SUBCULTURE

One of the outstanding features of the drug subculture in England is the almost total absence of Negro heroin and cocaine addicts. Schur found 1 Negro, and we have interviewed 1 in the present study; and although Hewetson and Ollendorf found 6 in their sample, it appears the Negroes do not follow the addiction pattern so dominant in the United States. Addicts interviewed in this study confirmed that Negro heroin and cocaine addicts were very rare. Negroes in London do smoke marijuana and in the words of one informant, 'I never heard of junkies in Jamaica, but man, everybody smokes "charge". I have heard of one, two, three Jamaican junkies, most of the others stay with the weed scene.'

On the other hand, there is a marked increase in the number of Canadian and American addicts coming to England. Although information is limited, addicts and professional workers believe that North American heroin and cocaine addicts started coming to England in the late 1950's, and continued to enter the country in a fairly steady stream, until about 1962 when the Home Office began deporting and tightening immigration procedures. Lindesmith[7] states: 'It was noted earlier that during the last several years the reported total of known addicts in Britain has increased from something over 300 to more than 500. (The actual figures for this period are 1959, 454; 1960, 437; 1961, 470; 1962, 532; 1963, 635; and 1964, 753.) The article indicates that a substantial portion of this increase is accounted for by an influx of Canadian users who had heard about the "British system".'[7] Of the 16 heroin and cocaine addicts in our survey, 3 were Canadian. Impressions from one (see Chapter 7) are as follows:

'I came to England to further my addiction without going to jail; I got drugs the same day I landed, from Dr. Z. I knew about this doctor and several others before arriving. I said I was an addict which I wasn't at the time, and told the doctor I was using 4 grains of heroin a day, and that, if possible, I would like to be treated as a "registered" addict. The doctor replied, "Certainly"; it was a shock, you know, I mean it was so easy to get it.'

No doubt the Canadian addicts have increased the number known to the Home Office, but this would not account for such a large increase since 1959. The point should also be made that many North American addicts would not be listed in the Home Office statistics since these 'do not include addicts normally resident outside the United Kingdom, but who receive supplies of dangerous drugs whilst visiting.'

Even though it is uncertain how many Canadian and American addicts came to England in the late 1950's, there is reason to suppose that they may have influenced the type of non-therapeutic addiction during this period. The addict of the late fifties and until about 1962 belonged to a drug subculture similar to those frequently described in the United States. Schur[9] on the other hand, says 'There has been no pronounced development of an addict subculture in Britain. Cohen has noted that the prerequisite for emergence of a subculture is "the existence in effective interaction with one another of a number of actors with similar problems of adjustment".'

There does exist considerable interaction between addicts in London. As a result of the limited sources of supply, addicts must enter into a communication network in order to ensure a steady supply of drugs. Also, addicts from that period had similar interests, such as jazz, art, and poetry. Furthermore, they used American jazz and addict argot. Schur said this about the use of addict jazz argot: '... apparently the familiar American usage is now spreading to small groups of jazz connected drug users in Britain ... there is no evidence that the use of argot is widespread'.[9] Yet, all the addicts interviewed by us use the addict jazz argot extensively, such as 'H' and 'horse' for heroin, 'C' and 'coke' for cocaine; they use 'scene', 'pad', 'square', and 'gig' for typical jazz terms, but just how British addicts developed these American patterns is uncertain. It appears that it was not so much through direct interaction with Americans and Canadians as it was an identification through literature and jazz with the American addict subculture. It would seem that the British jazz-orientated drug subculture was fairly well developed by 1955; yet this was before any great number of American or Canadian addicts had arrived in England. Two addicts in our sample described this subculture in the Soho area in 1955–1956. One of these addicts (see also Chapter 3) explains how he became addicted:

Addict: I think it was pretty well much the effect of hanging around jazz clubs in Town, and smoking weed, and coming into contact where there was an environment of hard drugs and other addicts.

Question: Would you say that most of the jazz groups took drugs or smoked weed?

Addict: The big majority, yes, jazz and drugs seem to go together for some reason in this country.

Question: Were there many Americans or Canadians around at this time?

Addict: Not at this time, no, it was a very rare thing to meet an American. The only time this would happen would be on the yearly exchange, the jazz exchange when the American jazz musicians came to this country, and we would go over there. This would be about the only time, but apart from that, few Americans or Canadians would be "registered" here; it was an unheard of thing, but then it seems an everyday occurrence now. There were a lot of musicians that took the stuff, but most smoked; there were some Americans, but mostly English cats were making the scene.

Thus it is possible that during the mid-1950's there existed a drug subculture similar to those found in large American urban areas, and that this subculture formed a social locus for persons susceptible to drug addiction.

A NEW TYPE OF DRUG ADDICT

Currently, in England, there has developed a second type of drug addict and abuser who is quite different from the earlier type. These 'new addicts' are concentrated in the teenage group, dress in the 'mod fashion' either 'beat' or 'gear', and they are more likely to be abusers of amphetamines rather than heroin addicts. This type of youngster first became apparent around 1960 and was resented by the older addicts, one of whom commented thus:

'Just a drag (*the new addict*), you know, because they don't take drugs because of some need or some personal defect. It's just a case of exhibitionism with them, you know, the fact that "I'm a registered addict, take me", kind of thing. They go around with long hair and dark glasses. The mod addict, this new crew came in, they go around with the hypodermic sticking out of their top pocket kind of thing, and just advertising the fact that they're on drugs, you know.'

The older addicts' distaste for this new 'breed' of addicts and abusers is probably more the result of generational differences, i.e. a negative attitude toward British youth in general. This new group of young addicts do show a different pattern in their relationship with drugs, as will be illustrated in the case histories of these youth presented in Chapters 4, 5, and 6.

These differences between the older and younger addicts have probably caused the public to become more aware of drug addiction, since the new type of addict is closely associate with the current youth rebellion. This has caused considerable concern even among the older addicts. What the older addicts fear, it seems, is that these newcomers will cause society to view them all as 'trouble makers' and, thus, bring further sanctions to bear on all addicts; in fact, the process so well described by Lemert who states, 'If the deviant acts are repetitive and have a high visibility, and if there is a severe societal reaction, which, through a process of identification is incorporated as part of the "me" of the individual, the probability is greatly increased that the integration of existing roles will be disrupted, and that re-organization based upon a new role or roles will occur'.[6]

Many of the older addicts, in an attempt to avoid this 'severe societal reaction' have attempted to disassociate from the younger addicts and abusers. As one said, 'I don't like the West End at all anymore.'

Terrence Morris, Editor of the *British Journal of Sociology*, has stated what he believes to be the crux of the British drug problem. He says:

'Schur writes, presumably of the United States, that in recent years there has been a considerable repudiation of the once prevalent dope fiend myth, which depicted the drug addict as a degenerate and vicious criminal much given to violent crimes and sex orgies, but this cannot be said to be true in Britain, where seaside riots by mods and rockers and press reports of police raids on coffee bars where purple hearts are bought and sold, have if anything, tended to reinforce the myth. Public attitudes towards the drug taker are highly coloured by the whole problem of generational conflict and the resentment of adults at the emergence of an adolescent culture that is reflected in a spectrum ranging from affluent pop singers to disorder on Bank Holiday beaches.'[8]

Future studies on British drug addiction will need to concentrate more on relationships between the adolescent subculture and the drug subculture, since the drug problem today centres in these British youngsters.

REFERENCES

1. *Drug Addiction: The Second Report of the Interdepartmental Committee* (1965) H.M.S.O., London.
2. Finestone, Harold (1957) Cats, Kicks, and Color. *Social Problems,* 5, 3–13.
3. Goffman, E. (1964) *Stigma.* Prentice-Hall, Englewood Cliffs, N.J. and London.
4. Hewetson, J., and Ollendorf, R. (1964) Preliminary Survey of 100 London Heroin and Cocaine Addicts. *Brit. J. Addic.,* 60, 110.
5. Kitsuse, John (1964) Societal Reaction to Deviant Behavior. *Social Problems,* 9, 247–256.
6. Lemert, E. M. (1951) *Social Pathology.* McGraw-Hill, New York and Maidenhead.
7. Lindesmith, A. R. (1965) *The Addict and the Law.* Indiana University Press, Bloomington.
8. Morris T. (1965) Book Reviews: Crime and Criminology. *Brit. J Sociol.,* 16, 368.
9. Schur, E. M. (1964) Drug Addiction Under British Policy. In Becker, Howard, S. (ed.) *The Other Side.* Collier-Macmillan, Glencoe and London.
10. Schur, E. M. (1963) *Narcotic Addiction in Britain and America.* Tavistock, London.
11. Wilkins, L. T. (1964) *Social Deviance.* Tavistock, London.
12. Winick, C., 'Physician Narcotic Addicts,' in Becker, Howard S. (see Ref. 9).

3 The Jazz Junkie

It was hard to tell how old George was. There was a hint of youth in his face, but this suggestion of youthfulness was quickly dismissed by a closer examination of George's facial features. His eyes, with their contracted pupils, seemed vacant, looking but seeing nothing. The gauntness of his face was accentuated by his high cheek bones, which were encased with tightly drawn, jaundice-coloured skin. George's face expressed tension and despair, as did the rest of his physical appearance. The whole of his slight body was maltreated, but what immediately drew an observer's attention were George's hands. The hands were discoloured from the constant presence of a cigarette and were burned from falling into a drugged sleep while holding a cigarette. It was not so much the actual appearance of the hands that attracted one's attention, but the fact that they were constantly moving; rubbing his neck and chest which had burns similar to those on the hands, running through his long black hair, handling and examining a cigarette, or scratching his forearms and ankles. The veins of his forearms and ankles were mapped by bluish scar tissue. These 'tracks' were the result of endless, and frequently unsanitary, 'fixes' or injections.

George looked 36. Yet, he was a 26-year-old heroin and cocaine addict. It took ten years of constant drug taking for his body to deteriorate to this degree. The following is the story of how George became like this.

JAZZ AND DRUGS

George came from a lower-middle class family. He remembered his early childhood as normal and on the whole, happy. Having done well in the 11-plus examinations, George went to a London grammar school. However, grammar school was not a happy experience for George; this may have been because the other students were from different backgrounds. They were not only different ethnically but in a different and higher socio-economic stratum than his. He did not assimilate well in school, nor did he do well in his studies. However, George resolved his unpleasant situation by turning to a more exciting and challenging outlet—jazz.

When George was 16, while still a student, he began working nights with a small jazz group in Soho. The money he earned did not amount to much, but he enjoyed playing jazz; and he was proud. Not many persons his age were playing professional jazz. Becoming more and more immersed in the jazz subculture, George began to consider school as an incidental and bothersome aspect of his life. He began to see less of his family with whom he was once close and, although his family desired him to finish school, George left before he was 17.

He was usually happy with his work and liked being independent. Yet, he would frequently become depressed; perhaps because he felt guilty for having disappointed his parents who had high aspirations for him, but his goals were different ones. George, with his colleagues, felt that his jazz was being impaired by these states of depression. He explains how this problem was resolved.

'My emotional state was interfering with my playing. So it was recommended by one of these addicts (*a member of the jazz group*) that I try "coc" (*cocaine*). To begin with, this depression which I was going through, I did find it going away from me. This cloud seemed to lift, and I felt as though I was playing better, and people seemed to be more interested in what I was saying.

'When I started, I started snorting cocaine through the nose. Later I found it was very expensive, apart from the fact that taking cocaine on its own can make you very physically sick if you don't mix it with heroin, you know. So I started intramuscular fixing, and from there, intravenous. After about three months of taking drugs, at first once in a while, then two or three times a week, and then, gradually, every day, I went to a doctor to get registered.'

To fully appreciate the almost nonchalant manner in which George began to take drugs, one must be aware of what the jazz scene in Soho was like in the mid-1950's. Here was a fairly small number of jazz musicians essentially isolated from the outside world. Their world revolved around jazz, and they were more concerned about their music than the larger-community attitudes towards them. This small subculture looked to its larger American counterpart for inspiration and guidance. Not only was British jazz similar to American, but its descriptive jargon and the subcultural norms were guided by it. At this time, one of the principal characteristics of the American jazz situation was drugs. It was commonly believed that drugs solved the emotional problems of jazz musicians and also helped them to express themselves better. The truth in this notion is dubious. A recent study has shown that jazz musicians do not take drugs as frequently as is assumed, nor do they believe drugs to be helpful to their work.[1] Few American jazz musicians were resident in Britain at this time, but American jazz was present in spirit and part of this spiritual pressure was the idea that drugs were beneficial for playing good jazz. Rightly or wrongly, this concept was accepted as true by George and other British musicians. As George described the situation:

'Jazz and drugs seem to go together for some reason in this country. Back then it (*drug usage*) was mostly confined to jazz, but there were quite a few prostitutes who were addicts and one or two writers who heard about drugs and wanted to experiment and got caught up . . . I think it was pretty much the effect of hanging around jazz clubs in town and smoking weed and coming into contact where there's an environment of hard drugs and other addicts.'

Thus, the cultural context in which George began his drug experience was, at best, neutral in its attitude toward it. Drugs were overtly used in an almost 'therapeutic' manner. Since this group was fairly well isolated from the community, the drug addicts were not faced with negative social sanctions which typically confront drug addicts in Western civilization. This 'vice' was hidden from the moral indignation of society.

George was pleased with the effect heroin and cocaine had on his music for about three years. He no longer experienced states of depression; the jazz group was playing well and often, and, on the whole, his world of jazz was rewarding and happy. However, this way of life was to end soon.

FROM JAZZ TO DRUGS

As George continued to take drugs, his 'habit' or dosage became larger and larger. He could no longer control the amount he took and found that drugs, not jazz, were becoming

2* 33

the central element in his life. This is the way George told of his shift from jazz to drugs:

'After a while, as drugs took hold of me, you know, when I wasn't able to use drugs but drugs started to use me up, one gets very unreliable in not turning up for rehearsals and practice, and not turning up on gigs (*jazz sessions*). You get a bad name and consequently start to go down.

'It took me about three years before agents started to shy away from me. I was just down to having to fight for one-night stands or two or three nights in Manchester or something like that, but never in any good-class jazz clubs. It was always second- and third-rate clubs where I could get gigs; this in itself started to depress me more. Consequently, the amount or dose of the drug I was taking obviously increased because of depression. So I just went from bad to worse, and to a "hand to mouth" kind of thing, you know, living off friends and other junkies.'

Four years after he began to take drugs, George no longer played jazz, nor did he care about jazz. Drugs had taken over as the dominant and driving force in his life. Sex, food, clothes work, parents—none of these things meant anything to George. He had moved from one subculture to another, from jazz to drugs.

THE DRUG SUBCULTURE

George was 20 years old when he quit the jazz scene for the drug scene. The following account covers a period of six years and shows what George considered were significant facets of his life. These aspects can be broken down into four areas of discussion—hustling, the British system, the ritual of fixing, and the changing drug scene.

HUSTLING

Hustling is a generic term which usually refers to any number of strategies addicts may use to obtain drugs. Since, for many addicts, almost every act is done in order to directly or indirectly get drugs, hustling becomes a way of life in which one's existence is dependent on maintaining his drug habit. In George's case, it is not exaggerating to say that drugs became not the principal driving force in his life, but the sole driving force. He was well aware of this fact, as shown in the following comment:

'Music just became nothing to me. At times I turned to crime, thieving art books from art shops or any way you can make money you know, to live and so on and so forth. It's just a case of stealing art books from one shelf to another (*crime*), you know, stealing radios or cameras from cars; anything, just hustling in general, never anything really big to get yourself sent down for a long time, if you were caught. You know, I mean 'cause you're just put away for a few months or on probation or sent to a hospital or something.'

* * *

'Quite often, there'd be a group of us who used to stay in one pad or else a derelict house or something like that. It's staying in groups or walking about, you know, going together in pairs, very rarely on their own at any time. Invariably, in a case like this, when a junkie is doing what is commonly known as skipping, when he's got nowhere to live, no room, no job, no regular income . . .'

* * *

'When you start taking "coc" with "horse" (*heroin*), you lose all self-interest, self-respect; you're not worried about what you look like, you know, or where you're going to sleep; whether you're going to sleep in a bed or in a park. These things don't matter.'

THE BRITISH SYSTEM

George and his fellow addicts were living, or existing, in the above manner when Britain did not have a drug problem and when American students of addiction were examining and praising the British system which had prevented the development of a drug subculture. In this system the addict was able to get drugs from doctors without financial or social liability. Yet, what George described suggests that the British system was not functioning in such an efficient way. Indeed, a central part of the hustling process was hustling the few doctors who dispensed drugs for addicts. In all, George had 13 doctors in this period of seven years Sometimes the doctors would break off the relationship because George refused to have his dosage cut down, because he could not pay his bills if the doctor were private, because his appearance in the waiting room caused complaints from other patients, because he had altered or stolen the doctor's prescription forms, or, because in general he was a nuisance. George, on the other hand, would seldom discontinue seeing a doctor as long as he could get drugs His description of his relationships with these many doctors illustrates the difficulty of both parties concerned to maintain a reciprocally beneficial relationship.

First, George tells why he got registered; this was mainly because it was more convenient and beneficial. He did not hesitate in getting registered, and, as stated earlier, did so only three months after he began to take drugs. This doctor was a private psychiatrist whose practice contained a fairly large number of addicts. George stayed with this doctor for three years. However, after his decline in jazz he was unable to pay the fee. This was the longest he ever stayed with any one doctor. He states:

'Before I got registered, the means to my drugs was the black market, other junkies. In this country there isn't any particular organized narcotics peddling. Any peddling that is done is by other addicts who get more than their daily need from the doctor. For instance, they go to a doctor and say, "You know, Doc, I take between 5 and 10 grains a day," when in effect they take only 5 grains. The other 5 they sell as a means of not having to go to work and for money to pay their rent and the usual things. This was my source of buying. If you got a good addict, a decent addict, invariably the kind of standard rate was a grain for £1. You used to get these bitches and bastards who, as soon as they saw you, the price went up. This didn't happen too often.

'When I got registered, I wasn't by any means addicted physically, although I felt a need for the drug. I wasn't going through any bad physical symptoms without the drug. There's no way the doctor can tell you're not addicted.'

However, after George became fully integrated into the drug subculture, he still would frequently have to buy drugs on the black market even though he was registered. This was because he could not control the amount of drugs he would take once he got his prescriptions. Typically, he would use all his prescription within a few hours instead of in the prescribed three or four days.

When he did 'blow' his 'scrip' (prescription) George would frequently try to get more drugs from his doctor rather than attempt to buy drugs from other addicts. Below, he tells what usually happened after he obtained his prescription.

'After I pick up the scrip from the chemist, I go to the nearest toilet, and I don't come out of the toilet until it's (*the drugs*) all gone. I mean every junkie does this. This is when hardships come in if you get a hard task doctor, or a doctor you can't pull the wool over his eyes very well; but on the whole, I've been lucky with doctors, although I've had to go to some extremes to get "stuff" from them, to get extra prescriptions. I've had as many as three or four scrips in one day for the same amount. Because I don't know, being an addict, one becomes a kind of psychologist or psychiatrist because it's from the action or reaction of the doctor that you know how you've been getting along, so you turn your story to please him and to suit him—providing he thinks he's doing you good.

'I remember on one occasion when things were getting hard with Dr. X, I went and jumped into the Serpentine (ornamental lake in Hyde Park) and arrived in his office dripping wet. I told him I'd been out boating and fell in and my stuff had fallen out of my pockets. The usual thing is putting matches under bottles, and they cracked from the heat (*heroin comes in a solid state; therefore addicts dissolve it in small bottles of water by heating it with matches*), or, you know, you haven't any place to stay, so the time you would have spent sleeping, you used up your extra stuff, and all that. Countless lies, really fantastic lies, are pulled. You eventually, you know, get a scrip out of him.'

George was, however, not always able to get a 'scrip' from doctors, no matter how exotic his story or how desperate his need. He was asked if his fellow addicts would assist him in getting drugs when he was in critical need of them. His reply was:

'Well, they do providing they know that they're not really cutting their own throats. How can I put it? If they're not really endangering themselves. But you can be going around with a junkie and be quite friendly with him, and all of a sudden you find your stuff gone. You know, there's no real friendship or togetherness with junkies.'

It is not known if a junkie ever took advantage of him. It is known that George frequently exploited other junkies. This may explain why he felt that addicts would hesitate in helping him even though they were friendly. One addict described George in the following way:

'He's the biggest con man I've ever seen, and I've seen some. You know, he's the type of person who can borrow something from you and never give it back. Yet, when he asks for something again, you give it to him. I let him stay in my pad for three weeks; that guy has no responsibility. You know, he would shoot a whole scrip at one time and then roll around the floor almost dying when he ran out. I let him borrow some of my clothes when he was down. That's the last I've seen him or my clothes. He's not a bad guy, but junk ruined him.'

George was very frank about the behaviour that is condemned outside the drug subculture. He readily admitted such things as altering prescriptions and petty thievery. However one type of deviancy, behaviour frowned upon by addicts and non-addicts alike, that George was ashamed of, was pushing drugs. The term 'pusher' did not accurately describe the illicit British seller of drugs at this time. Like most drug terms, it was

37

adapted from the American experience. In the United States, the pusher is the main means by which drugs are obtained by addicts. The American pushers handle huge amounts of drugs and receive a great deal of money for 'cut' or very impure drugs. They have an infamous reputation for taking advantage of addicts even though they are frequently addicts themselves; the negative connotation of this term has been accepted by the British addicts. As a result, they will only admit selling drugs illicitly after they qualify their confession. Their qualifications usually entail statements that suggest that drugs are sold only to known addicts who are in short supply. However, in practice, addicts must sell drugs to non-addicts; otherwise there would be no perpetuation of the addict subculture. New members have to be supplied drugs. This is the way George described his experience in selling drugs.

'Personally, I haven't (*pushed*). Well, when I say I haven't sold . . . I mean never sold enough to get money for rent or food or anything. If I was at the chemist and this junkie has missed his doctor, I mean, I'd sell it to him. That's as far as I've gotten to selling personally. I don't think anybody, well, maybe I stick my neck out when I say this, but I don't think any real addict in this country sells for profit because there's no need for it. In the States you've got to push to survive, to get your junk. This doesn't exist in this country, so, therefore, it cancels itself out, I guess.'

One might ask at this point, 'Why hadn't George tried to get a cure or why hadn't someone forced him to get some kind of treatment, especially since he had seen 13 different doctors?' George did have a number of 'cures' (treatment for addiction). Unfortunately, though, cures are not usually successful for addicts; this seemed to be true for George. He had a total of 22 cures. Some of these cures were voluntary, others were involuntary, that is, under court order. Some were short, others long. A few were in private establishments; most of them were in public institutions. The type of treatment varied almost as much as the number of cures. The one thing they all had in common is that they failed. George could not say why these cures had failed. He no longer cared, for he was convinced that he would never be cured. Indeed, he felt that it was impossible for any addict to be cured in the true sense of the word. This was an accepted part of the addict's world to George. Some of his cures were the result of having been arrested for some drug offence or another minor crime. Yet, at other times these arrests led not to treatment, but to incarceration in prison. He was sent to prison five times—twice for breaking into a chemist shop, twice for altering prescriptions, and once for stealing a car radio.

Thus, for George the British system did not work. For various reasons, some his fault, some the doctors', he was unable to establish the necessary rapport with doctors that would enable him to maintain a steady supply of drugs. For many reasons treatment was unsuccessful in arresting his addiction. And for a number of equally varied reasons George was sometimes sent to treatment centres by the courts as a sick person, while at other times he was sent to prison as a criminal, thus reflecting the true ambivalence of the British system.

THE RITUAL OF FIXING

George had been taking drugs for approximately seven years when he began to notice that he no longer got a 'kick' or 'flash' from taking drugs. The quantity of drugs he was taking daily had grown to a very large amount. His body had developed such a tolerance for narcotics that it took a huge dose before he could get any pharmacological effect from them. George very seldom got such a huge dosage. Unable to get a buzz from the drugs George began to get a kick from the acts necessary for injecting the drugs. A certain mystique developed around the acts of 'cooking-up' (heating and dissolving the drugs in water) and 'fixing' or 'flushing'. He described what this ritual meant to him.

'After an addict has been using stuff for quite some time, he no longer gets this so-called flash from the drug itself. His main kick is the actual making up of the drug, the hitting of the vein, and watching this kind of flower-like—the blood hitting the water. This, to him becomes something personal, so when he goes into a hospital and it's done cold and clinically, he gets nothing at all from it. I mean, the fix may be exactly the same amount, but the fact that he hasn't cooked it, hasn't hit the vein, he hasn't watched the blood coming counteracts any kind of feeling of joy. It takes the kick out of it. This is what I mean by becoming a ritual to an addict.

'This, to ordinary people, may sound kind of masochistic, but it's about the only kick a junkie gets unless he has a terrible lot (*of drugs*), unless he's addicted to some ridiculous (*high*) amount, which he wouldn't get from anyone. I get this intense pleasure of hitting, especially if there is a non-junkie, some middle-class person there. You know, I don't know if this was whether I wanted to shock them or what it was.'

It appears that George and other addicts attempt to find a functional equivalent to the pharmacological effect of the drugs. They do this by emphasizing not the drug, but the highly personal acts associated with giving themselves the drugs.

THE CHANGING DRUG SCENE

George became addicted in the mid-1950's. At that time there were few addicts, and these few were hidden from the public scrutiny. However, during the ten years he was an addict George witnessed a change in the drug scene. Besides the actual number of addicts increasing, he felt that the type of person becoming addicted changed. George began to notice this transition in 1961. He said:

'There was a lot of publicity in the papers about different raids the police were making; hemp started coming into the public eye quite a bit, and, you know, a lot of these so-called "teddy boys". This fad was dying, but at the time (*they*) were looking around for something new. Well, I guess drugs was their best bet. This was a way of proving themselves.

'They're (*new type of addict*) just a drag, you know, because they don't take drugs because of some need or some personal defect. It's just a case of pure exhibitionism with them, you know, the fact that "I'm a registered addict, take me" kind of thing. They go around with the long hair and dark glasses with a hypodermic sticking out of their top pocket kind of thing, and just advertising the fact that they're on drugs, you know.'

*   *   *

'Between the older addicts there was this comradeship, this togetherness, you know, one would help the other out without necessarily having to be his best friend. But today, I mean, you can go to the chemist, and you can stand there all night and be sick as a dog, and nobody would offer to help you out. When I started, this just didn't happen.'

*   *   *

'The majority of them get registered without even taking drugs. I literally mean this; you know, there's no way by which a doctor in this country can tell whether a person is addicted or not. Some ask to look at your arm, and some don't even bother. In a lot of cases a cat will fix a half a pill (*1/12th of a grain*) and get registered the next day for 5 grains. This happens quite a lot, and I think this has happened with the majority of these kids.'

*   *   *

'These kids, they can give up working in a factory, or, you know, and sell what they don't use (*drugs*), pay the rent and buy good suits and all the rest of it, I guess. I think this thing of, you know, I'll take about

40

5 grains each (*heroin and cocaine*) with their enlarged pupils and their sharp suits, dressed up a bit, you know, fat and healthy at the same time, you know, well, it's sickening to see it and listen to it all. And, apart from the fact that it is making the whole thing, well, bringing the whole thing out into the public in a distorted way, you know, the junkie who does rely on his daily dose and causes nobody any trouble, he's the guy who eventually gets the kick in the backside; he's the one who's going to feel it because of these kids who are just rebelling against their mothers and fathers.'

There are elements of truth in what George said, as can be seen by contrasting his story with those in Chapter 6. The typical addicts of the fifties are different from those of the sixties. Still, he has probably exaggerated the discrepancy between the 'old' and 'new' type of addict. His rather romantic recollection of the older type and his negative description of the younger type were at least in part brought about by the difference in age between George and the younger addicts. Also, and more important, is his obvious distaste for the negative publicity the younger addicts have given to addiction. George feared and realized that the more addiction comes into the public eye, the more frequent and harder will be the sanctions against addicts. This, in turn, means that drugs will be more difficult to obtain. His analysis has proved to be a correct one.

DEATH

George was very concerned about death. Several times he had been near death from an overdose of drugs. Many of his addict friends had died early in life. An early death was an accepted part of his life. Indeed, George and some of his friends developed a rather morbid game concerning death, called the rotary. He explained the game with some excitement:

'You see, a group of us started (*taking drugs*) around the same time. I don't know, through the taking of drugs and one thing and another, there is a kind of a rotary; as one dies, you know, everyone looks to the next one, you know, a kind of measurement. John's been on a year more than me, then I'm the next one to go since John's died; and this is the pattern. I mean, often one can be pointed out in town as, well, you know, "this one's the next to go" kind of thing. One gets kind of, or becomes, especially to the youngsters now, as a king figure, you know, of junk.'

41

George thought he was the 'king figure of junk'. But he no longer feels this way. He hanged himself in prison. He died at the age of 26, and he had been an addict for eleven years.

REFERENCE

1. Winick, C. (1960) The Use of Drugs by Jazz Musicians. *Social Problems*, **7**, 240–253.

4 The Purple Heart Craze

Stimulant drugs, particularly the amphetamines, have become extremely popular with the youth in Great Britain over the last few years. The most frequently used is Drinamyl, or, in the slang of the teenagers, Purple Hearts, because of their original shape and colour. In 1964, because of their abuse, amphetamines were subjected to restrictions (see Chapter 2, p. 13).

Originally, these stimulants or 'pep pills' were used extensively by females who were on weight-reduction diets. There is no doubt that some youth became introduced to these pills through their mothers who had a constant supply. In London, Liverpool, and the industrial towns of the Midlands, the youth began to take the Purple Hearts to stay awake and maintain their energy during a weekend in the town, from Friday or Saturday evening to Monday morning. These pills are bought from other youth at the ubiquitous coffee bar and clubs in the larger cities at prices ranging from 6d. to 1s 6d per tablet. Large numbers of these pills may be consumed in a twenty-four hour period.

Physiologically, unlike other stimulants, amphetamine used to excess leads to tolerance so that larger numbers may be taken which cause loss of appetite, restlessness, palpitations, and insomnia. Abuse may lead to delusions of persecution (fortunately reversible), which the users sometimes describe as the 'horrors'. Of course, some Purple Heart users never progress beyond abuse of this drug; others become smokers of marijuana, and still others become users of the hard drugs of heroin and cocaine.

In this chapter we will present some typical cases of amphetamine abuse, in which progression to other drugs does and does not occur.

MIKE: WORLD ALONE

World Beyond

What's in this world of might,
Which creates such wonderful foundations of sight,
By thoughtless thoughts, we try to ease burdens
By shifting into unconscious,
Wondering whether we'll awake in the morn,
To see the rising of the sun or just a flicker of light.

The conscious is not aware of the dangers,
Ah! The subconscious is working on the facts,
The brain functions and wonders what makes us tick.
What is this sudden inspiration in youth
Which seems like streaks of mirror lightning intruding into
    my skin.
If only I could get beyond the mysteries of life,
Oh! I feel so sick.

This poem, 'World Beyond', and 'Moods', which is printed at the end of this section, were given to one of the authors on one of his frequent visits to England by a young amphetamine abuser named Mike. Only 15 years of age at the time, Mike had tremendous creative talents which he expressed through poetry and sculpture.

SOCIAL BACKGROUND

Mike first came to our attention in a treatment unit for drug addicts and abusers in an English hospital about two years ago. At 15 he was the youngest patient, having come to the unit under an alias; he had false identity papers which passed him for 19 years of age. He had appeared before the court for having forged a prescription for amphetamines. The judge, an understanding man, had given him a choice of volunteering for treatment for his excessive use of Purple Hearts or serving a term in a correctional institution. He had chosen the former alternative.

From Northern Ireland, Mike had left school on his 15th birthday; his rural town offered few opportunities for work, and he migrated to London to find a job. His social/economic background was working-class, his father being employed as an agricultural labourer. Mike was the eldest of five children. The emotional atmosphere of his family was permeated by his father's excessive drinking, the mother's ill health, and the constant economic deprivations which buffeted them.

Mike characterized himself as being hypersensitive as a child. He states, 'I was always more aware than the other children of life—of nature, hurts, emotions, and feelings. . . . I seemed to feel more happiness and more pain than others.' Mike was different from other members of the family who read little and discussed intellectual matters rarely. His performance at school was good; he read extensively and began to write verse but received little encouragement from his family. They urged him to leave school, go to work and obtain a job to support himself. It can be conjectured that in a more permissive environment he would have been supported in his desire to develop his innate talents.

LONDON: MYSTERIES OF LIFE

A few days after his 15th birthday, Mike arrived with his battered brown suitcase in London to find a job, ill-prepared to cope with the urban environment. He succeeded in obtaining a job as a messenger and shared quarters with another youth from Ireland. His recollection of his first weeks in London is one of pervasive loneliness. He states, 'There were thousands of people around, but no one to talk to—no one seemed to care about me or what I thought'.

His introduction to amphetamines occurred on a visit to a coffee bar in central London with his roommate. Taken at first on weekends, these pep pills seemed to him to alleviate his sense of depression and loneliness. Within a period of a few months, his intake of amphetamines had increased to around 20 per day until he was arrested for forging a prescription for them. However, he had never smoked marijuana nor had he taken heroin or cocaine; thus his only drug experience was with amphetamines.

Within six months of his coming to London, Mike was in a treatment unit for addicts. His adjustment within the unit was excellent and his prognosis was good when we first met him.

MIKE: THE CREATIVE SPIRIT

The first time we met Mike was in the treatment unit; he was seated on a hardback chair with his coat on, intensively absorbed in reading poetry. We asked him if he liked poetry, and he said, 'Yes, and I also write poetry'. We began to talk about poetry and poets—Keats, Auden, and Eliot. He also stated that he liked to make things and removed from his locker a figure which he had carved in soap. Composed of three pieces of soap, his figure had been entitled by him, 'Stages of Life'. The bottom piece, in which was carved the face of a child, was representative of infancy; the middle piece, which contained two faces parallel to each other, one smiling, the other depressed, represented the split of adolescence; and the upper piece had etched in it the face of an old man representing adulthood. This figure, of course, is symbolic of Mike and his quest for his identity in adolescence—whether he will become the well-adjusted youth so glorified in the mass media and represented by his smiling face, or whether he will retreat further into his loneliness and introspection represented by his depressed facial carving.

The next time we visited the unit (about a week later) with a visiting physician, Mike was sitting at a table in the corner. This shy young boy was dressed in a soiled white shirt whose sleeves were turned up two times, and the neck was open. He wore a pair of dark mohair trousers, tight around the hips, with side pockets and tapering in the stovepipe style. When Mike saw us he went to his locker and removed a notebook and brought it into the Day Room where we were conversing with the other addicts. He hovered near us, not entering the conversation, until we asked him how his poetry was coming. He then showed us his book, and we sat down at a table, and he began to read to us from his composition book his poems in his Irish brogue. We commented that we liked the poems, and his eyes sparkled with happiness as he presented two of his handwritten poems as a gift.

These poems speak for themselves; the first, 'World Beyond', and the other, 'Moods', at the end of this section should not be over-analysed. They reflect the search of a sensitive teenager for meaning and purpose in life which has been harsh to him. They also show the human spirit in action, and the changing mood swings in the adolescent personality as he confronts new experiences daily.

Moods

I can't think in this despairing mood.
As I come nearing I feel the heat

The Purple Heart Craze

Just like sweating or freezing,
I have sunk into moods beyond boredom.
If only I had the fantasies of freedom,
Then I would be converted far from resentment
Just to see the seven wonders of this world
Or just to see the snails slowly
Plunging into this rebellious earth
Which is full of life, lasting life.

ALICE: GOOD-TIME GIRL

Alice is an 18-year-old, single, white female, who is currently being treated for amphetamine abuse at a private institution in England. She recently came to the attention of authorities in London because of the illegal possession of Purple Hearts. First, she was sent to a hostel and later to the private treatment centre.

Alice is an attractive teenager who looks several years older than her age, although her manner is still that of a youngster. When we talked with her she was dressed in a tight black sweater, a mini-skirt, and long red hose with a circular pattern on them. Her hair was worn long and hung over both sides of her face which wore no makeup.

FAMILY BACKGROUND

Alice was born in Europe but came to England with her family when she was a small child. At 6 years of age, her father died. She describes her childhood as being fairly happy, but she states, 'I did not like to spend nights at home when I was older; I wanted to go out, which my mother did not like'.

Her school performance was erratic. She indicated, 'I was never good in school. I always played truant except for art and drama classes in which I was always interested.' Her mother took her out of school when she was 15 years of age. She obtained a job in an outlying London area.

INTRODUCTION TO DRUGS

Alice states the first time she saw people using drugs was on a 'Ban the Bomb' March in which she participated shortly after her 15th birthday. At the same time she began to frequent

47

coffee bars in Hampstead, and became less and less under the control of her mother.

By this time she had seen quite a few of her friends smoking 'hemp'. One night she decided (on her own) to try some marijuana. She said, 'I knew some friends that took it (*marijuana*); I asked them for some; they asked another friend and he sold it'. Alice was asked to describe the type of persons that used and sold her the marijuana; this she found difficult because she had never really thought about it. However, after some deliberation she stated that most of them were in their early teens and twenties; she summarized their characteristics by saying 'They're beats, I guess'.

At the age of 16, approximately a year after Alice started smoking marijuana, she was introduced to Purple Hearts. She was well aware of what Purple Hearts were and what they were supposed to do for or to you, namely, to get you 'high'. Several of her friends were taking them and while at a West End club she tried to find someone who might sell her some. She learned of a boy in his early twenties who had some to sell; the actual transaction took place on a side street in the Soho area. This person became a regular 'contact' for Alice. She would meet him at approximately the same time and place each week, but he did not always come. She never knew the person's name. He was a young, white man in his early twenties and (she thinks) a cocaine-heroin addict.

As yet she has not experimented with hard drugs. She states, 'I had a lot of chances to try "horse" (*heroin*), but I would not try it. I've got a terrible lack of will-power, I have.' But whether she will in the future, after discharge, is of course, another question.

DYNAMICS OF OBTAINING MARIJUANA AND PURPLE HEARTS

Alice was asked how people usually obtained marijuana. She said, 'Sorta have to know the people, you just go to a certain coffee bar and just sit and wait for it. The peddlers would come up and ask you after they had a good look at you.'

Concerning Purple Hearts, she states: 'Bit more difficult; you go in a coffee bar, see the "contact" and ask if anyone is selling P.H. Keep looking and you'll find someone. Sometimes you might get a fake P.H.' We asked her if she had ever been given any or if she knew of anyone who had. 'No, but I've heard about it. You get Purple Hearts in a little brown packet of 10, but you never know if you're getting 9 or 8, or 10, or some of it might be broken up and every little bit counts. You must open them up immediately to see what you've got.' Concerning the price of Purple Hearts, 'If you know a friend, you can get 10 for 10s'. Alice was vague concerning the source of Purple Hearts, saying that she felt almost all the peddlers were users who got their supply from their general practitioner. However, she was not certain on this point. (*Most 'pep pills' sold illicitly stem probably from theft from factories etc.*) Alice said there had been a few times when she could not get a supply of P.H.; then she 'used to take stuff from the chemist . . . things that would turn me on . . . cough medicine, anything'.

PARTIES

Before being apprehended by the police, Alice's life centred around going to parties and to the clubs and coffee bars in London. Parties generally take place in the flats of friends of hers on week-ends, and on weekday nights she spends a large amount of time in the West End clubs. On a typical week-end, Alice leaves home early on Saturday afternoon and goes to coffee bars in Hampstead where she meets her friends. There, in her words, they '. . . get a list of parties to go to . . . then we leave and go to a party, then another party, then another one, then another . . . before you know it, the night's gone'.

Alice added, 'When I went to a party, I'd mix P.H., drinks and smoke (*marijuana*); this would put me on quite well. . . . They always had the best records there—blues, beat records, mostly.' The other people at the parties, Alice said, were mainly 'beat type of people, some a little older than 20'. According to her, quite a few were on heroin and cocaine, most smoked reefers, but not too many were on Purple Hearts.

Alice spent most of her weekday evenings in the clubs and coffee bars of London's West End. Her favourite club was the *X* Club which charged an admission fee. This club has a juke box in a large room with tables. In the room there seems to be a mixture of people; addicts, non-addicts, and a few tourists. (According to her, many of the people 'look arty, but aren't really arty; there are a lot of mods in them'.) Adjoining this room is a smaller, darkly-lit room, which just has benches along the wall. Alice says of this room, 'A few teenagers are taking Purple Hearts ... you may not see them taking them but they're always going to the other room for water; you know what they're doing'. This second room, which has music piped in from the juke box, is filled with drug addicts and abusers. Adjoining this room is still a smaller and darker room with nothing but planks on the floor. Alice was not sure what this room was used for but assumed it was for sleeping (Little imagination is needed to suggest other uses.)

ALICE: THE FUTURE

Although Alice has been at the private treatment centre several months and is scheduled for discharge soon, the outlook is problematic. She states that she wants to stop taking drugs, but feels that she must change her whole way of life in order to stay away from the sources of the drugs. This will be difficult, for she told us, 'If someone offered me some Purple Hearts today, I'd probably take them'. In fact, at the treatment centre she and two other girls, while on a week-end leave, did visit a chemist and bought some patent medicine in an attempt to get high. The result, however, was that all got sick.

Her plans for the future, while vague, are rather unrealistic. She states, 'I'd like to get a good job. I'd also like to go to art school. I don't know what I'll do.' She has no occupational skills to offer on the labour market and minimal financial resources to support any art school studies. This poverty of occupational, financial and, from our analysis, emotional resources makes Alice, like so many other youth, unfortunately an excellent candidate for further progression into the drug way of life.

LAURA: RAPID PROGRESSION IN DRUGS

Laura is also currently undergoing treatment for drug abuse. In a short period of six months she became introduced to hashish, Purple Hearts, and had her first injections of heroin. This is a more rapid progression in drugs than is usually the case. For example, George and Glatt[1] reported that of 90 young male heroin and cocaine addicts treated by them, the average age of starting on amphetamines had been 16·5 years, on cannabis 16·9, and heroin and cocaine 18·6 years. Corresponding ages in 11 cases of young female addicts to heroin and cocaine had been 15·8, 15·5 and 20·6 years.

The psychiatrist did not consider that Laura had yet become an addict since she had taken only small amounts of heroin for a short period of time. When arrested by the police in Soho for illegal possession of a syringe and marijuana, she was first sent to a correctional institution and later was transferred to a private treatment centre.

FAMILY BACKGROUND

Laura is an 18-year-old white female, who is quite attractive, well mannered, and very friendly. In the current London style her hair is long, and when we talked with her she was wearing a simple housecoat. Despite having been involved with drugs for only six months, she considers herself an expert.

Laura is an adopted child of a wealthy and highly respected English family. Her childhood, she believes, was a happy one in that her parents gave her anything that she asked for, but she resented the constant comparisons that her parents made between her and her older sister who was not adopted. Her parents were always telling Laura to follow in the steps of her older sister, which to her meant going to debutante parties which she considered a drag. In her home town she did quite well in school, and at age 18 her parents enrolled her in an art school in London.

INTRODUCTION TO DRUGS

Her room-mate at school took sleeping pills and one evening offered some to Laura. Apparently, the room-mate did not take these pills in excess. Laura continued to take a great quantity of sleeping pills for two weeks and then stopped. She doesn't know what kind of pills these were nor the reason she took them, stating, 'They made me feel better, I guess. I don't know why.' Although Laura does not know exactly why she took her room-mate's pills, she stopped taking them when she was introduced to 'hash'.

Laura started going to West End clubs when she arrived in London, and later supplemented this form of entertainment by going to 'pads' in the Chelsea area. It was at one of these pads that a boy Introduced her to hash. The boy was white, American, and in his early twenties. The actual introduction was very casual. The boy simply asked Laura if she wanted to try some hash. Laura said, 'yes', and the boy gave her a reefer he had made up. She said she didn't know the boy 'that well', rather he was just a casual friend. The people at this particular party were fairly young (in their early twenties), mostly white, but there were a few West Indians. Laura's escort at this party was an American, which led her to comment: 'I used to think it cool to talk like Americans. Some people like to dress, smoke, and do everything like Americans.'

We asked where the hashish and marijuana at this specific party came from, but Laura started speaking in general terms and telling of her personal experience and knowledge of drug trafficking. She first described the source of the cannabis:

'The big pushers were coloured ... they've been all around the world and import it by various methods and things. They used to get it in by wood and that sorta thing. Coloured people only touch that (*hemp*), they don't go in for that at all (*hard drugs*) ... They're (*the coloured*) users themselves, but they view it as a business ... the big ones, not the hustlers.'

Laura, who buys cannabis only in bulk, states, 'The only people that buy it in reefers are mods. They wouldn't buy it in bulk because they wouldn't know what to do with it. They couldn't smoke it.' At this point Laura started laughing in a knowing fashion.

Laura's experience with Purple Hearts has been limited, she says, because 'I don't like pills at all. They charge about 1s and 1s 6d apiece now. At one time they used to only cost about 9d. They have been cheap to get ... six for a shilling.' Furthermore she stated:

'P. H. (*Purple Hearts*) are hard to find now and expensive, but you can get it all right. X Club gives out more glasses of water than any place in London. I always have seen people, mostly kids, come up to men in the streets and ask for some P.H. It's much easier to get "weed" from the coloured. You go into a cafe or something, and they'll ask, "Are you all right?" and you know what they want ... These cafes are around Notting Hill Gate; I stayed in a pad just off of there.'

INTRODUCTION TO COCAINE AND HEROIN

At one of the parties she attended in her first months in London she sniffed some cocaine through the nostrils, which she found a pleasurable experience, but it was hard for her to get it, for as she says, 'People always want to keep their "coc".'

Approximately two weeks before she was arrested she had her first heroin. She states:

'Heroin is very difficult to get hold of. Sometimes there are a dozen police all around. The "fuzz" (*police*) can give you a hard time ... I got my "horse" (*heroin*) from the beats of *X* Club since there're many junkies among the beats ... Most of them were registered.'

Laura feels that an addict who really needs a 'fix' would have no difficulty in obtaining one, for her view of the addict sub-culture is still essentially a romantic one. She states:

'Addicts always help each other. If you ask around in the right places, they'll get it (*drugs*) for you in about half an hour. The worst time is when you haven't enough money, but you always get it. Sometimes it's a little harder than others.'

Furthermore, drug usage is pervasive, she says, in her friends, many of whom were active in the 'Ban the Bomb' movement or considered themselves beatniks. According to her, 'Most of them are interested in hemp. They take smoking quite seriously.'

THE FUTURE

What will happen to Laura when she leaves the treatment centre? Occupationally, she wants to design and print theatrical props, although she has no specific plans in view. Perhaps she will return to art school. Her family is still strongly support-tive of her, psychologically and financially, and this offers hope for her therapeutically. Her attitude, as expressed in the following: 'I've given my parents a hard time, and they've done an awful lot for me. I've been treated as their own child,' shows well-balanced guilt feelings about her behaviour.

Counterbalancing this are her admittedly ambivalent feelings towards hard drugs. When discussing them she states:

'The ultimate high is heroin. I'm sorry I tried it because I'll never enjoy smoking again. It's quite likely I'll go on smoking ... I don't like alcohol, besides it's (*hemp*) not addictive; it's a lot better than alcohol ... doesn't have ill effects.'

But Laura is also aware that almost invariably anyone who intravenously injects hard stuff becomes an addict. At the interview's close her desire to stay off heroin when she returns to the community seems intense, for she says:

'I don't want to try "horse" again. They (*the police*) have been out to get registered addicts who push. I want to avoid that as much as I can. I won't go back to heroin.'

REFERENCE

1. George, H. R. and Glatt, M. M. (1967) A Brief Survey of a Drug Dependency Unit in a Psychiatric Hospital, *Brit. J. Addic.*, **62**, 147–153.

5 'Smoking' and 'Tripping'

A PRIVATE REVOLUTION—PETER

Cannabis, variously known as hashish, charge, hemp, marijuana, gear, kief, Mary Jane, pot, stuff, tea, weed, and grass, is currently the subject of much argument and speculation. As the WHO Expert Committee on Dependence-producing Drugs points out,

'There is no development of physical dependence, nor unequivocal proof that lasting mental disturbances have been produced by cannabis, although predisposed people may have temporary psychoses.'

Cannabis therefore seems to offer to protagonists clamouring for reform the benefits without the disadvantages of other dependence-producing substances. However, in spite of recent activity directed at a change in the law regarding it, it seems that the dangers to a minority of users are considerable, and that to most young users the association of cannabis with other more dangerous substances presents them with the idea that drugs are safe if used correctly—'Charge never hurt anybody'.

The Latey Report on the Age of Majority (published in London in July 1967) pinpoints a factor of great importance regarding our fast-moving society of today.

'Young people, as the old never tire of remarking, are not what they were. They are largely literate and educated; they are better off financially and far more independent of their parents; they are taught to think and inquire for themselves and mostly do so, and their experience of life is wider. The question is not whether this is a good or bad thing, but what are we to do about it?'

This literacy, independence and curiosity can give rise to a conflict between ambition and loyalty. At a time of natural uncertainty, young people must balance talent and knowledge that, in many cases, is greater than that of their parents against the spectrum of social background, perhaps a different mode of speech, a wider vocabulary, seemingly rigid parental attitudes, pride, love, sexual freedom, shame, and a double behaviour pattern—at home and away from home.

PETER

Peter comes from a modest, lower middle class home. His father is an inspector on the buses and his mother has not worked since she married; he has a brother two years younger than himself. From an early age Peter showed promise at school, and gained a scholarship to grammar school at the age of 11 years. He did well, stayed on to take A level exams, and warmed to the prospect of a future made richer by education. He gave of his best in English literature and decided quite early that he wanted to teach that subject. He was drawn towards a new world that was less attractive to his young brother.

The younger boy was much closer to his parents both in mentality and interests. Peter had been jealous of him from his early childhood and resented the fact that his brother was sometimes held up as a paragon for him to emulate. To his parents he probably presented grounds for both pride and confusion. They had always encouraged him to go as far as he could academically and had given what help they could. Their support was solid and certainly demanded sacrifice and faith, for higher education was a luxury denied them. They had, by careful budgeting, always had a comfortable home. When Peter was 7 years old they had been able to buy a small semi-detached house on a large mortgage, but had never aspired to a car; a television set came after the children had finished school, as did the few other luxury items in their home.

During adolescence Peter found himself out of phase with family and the established order of society. 'Respectability' and the quiet pride of his parents in their modest achievements began to annoy him and he started looking for short cuts to maturity: CND and other minority protests, dreams of revolutionary non-violent change, and the belief that his generation was to save Britain from itself.

Towards the end of his school career he began to feel the pressure of discipline in study. His first impulse was to give up: 'I felt that if I wasn't accepted as I was, then I wasn't prepared to go on. The discipline was knocking the enjoyment out of the subject.' At this point he was offered a place at a red-brick university and accepted it, confident that the real life was about to begin. He found, on going up to university, that he was to think and to write critical essays; the environment was new to him and for the first time he discovered that he was expected to discipline himself. He was stimulated by the free exchange of ideas, and the relationships he developed exposed him to many new situations. He began to explore new fields, one of which was the romanticized world of jazz and drugs. He was 18 years old, looking for any new experience, and his resolve to try hash stemmed from reading an article in *The Guardian* about the legalization of marijuana.

'It struck me as rather interesting and, at the same time, it was against the law. I had heard arguments against drugs, but this was the first time I had considered arguments in favour of their use. I felt I would like to gain personal experience.'

The chance to try 'pot' came soon afterwards when, in Edinburgh, he heard that someone could get hold of some 'stuff'; he clubbed together with three other students to buy some. They smoked it in a flat in the city and found it disappointing. However, Peter had felt that he should not expect too much from the first smoke and determined to persevere when the next chance came along. It came about a month later under similar circumstances and, as there was more hash on that occasion, he used it several times. He says, 'This time I began to derive a lot of pleasure from it, so much so that I decided to make contacts that would ensure a regular supply'.

At this time he was smoking whenever he could get supplies; sometimes weekly, sometimes monthly. By the following summer he was using it every day. The prospect of the coming long vacation led his thoughts towards a visit to Morocco, where he knew that he could buy hashish cheaply. It had also crossed his mind that he could finance the journey by selling (at reasonable profit) some hash which he intended to smuggle back to England.

He remembers the summer as one of semi-oblivion; he had vague dreams about essays he intended to write, and seemed on numerous occasions, to be on the point of discovering a new truth but, in fact, he produced nothing. He smoked his way across Europe, arriving back in England in September by way of Paris. Here he had been offered some pills (amphetamine) which he took with his hash. 'They perked me up for a few hours, which enabled me to enjoy my smoking a bit longer.'

It was at this stage that he had his first contact with heroin and cocaine users. When asked whether he felt he would have gone on to heroin and cocaine, he replied, 'I was very much put off the first time I saw somebody taking a fix. I was nauseated by the sight for a good while. I had the feeling nevertheless that I might be on the way there by the end of the summer; I don't know how much longer I would have lasted before I would have tried to mainline. Being realistic now (*after some weeks in hospital*), I was high so much of the time on hashish that I think it would have been six months at the most before the time had come when I would have felt that I needed something else to boost me beyond this state.' He also felt that if he went back on to hashish after discharge from hospital he would go through the same stages again, coming back to the point where he felt he needed a bigger kick.

He returned to university in October with a considerable quantity of Moroccan hashish. It had cost him £6 and was worth about £50 in the U.K.—more if he had been prepared to break it up and sell it in small quantities. Things went well for a few days until he returned to his room to find the police there with a search warrant. He had never kept his smoking quiet, he had no feeling of shame about it; but, on his own admission, his behaviour had slowly changed and he had become withdrawn and lazy, doing very little work at all. Perhaps most significantly he had noticed that he had arrived at a point where he no longer smoked for pleasure and relaxation with others but withdrew, under stress, to solitary smoking 'feeling a need' for stuff. 'I would give anything, would go out of my way, to get hashish.'

He was sent down from university and was charged with illegal possession; he entered hospital the following week. He settled down well in the hospital group, gained considerable insight and became active in discussions, art therapy and in plans for his future. He made a number of important discoveries about himself and about society He decided that personal change and adjustment had to come before change in society, and that he should make haste more slowly. Peter admitted that by using hash he was getting further away from even short-term solutions. After three months he felt able to cope with the outside world again. The Court had put him on a year's probation, which he accepted as a chance to restore his credit. He was troubled by one or two bouts of depression springing from the contemplation of renewed communication difficulties with his parents, but this proved easier than he had expected.

Peter was of very high intelligence, a fact confirmed by the clinical psychologist on several types of test. He applied for reinstatement and was taken back by his university almost on the first anniversary of being apprehended on the drug offence. In this twelve-month period he had come to terms with a hashish habit that had risen to a maximum of 1 pound a week—by his own definition it was a real dependence; he had realized that much of his past behaviour had created more problems than it had solved, and he had started to believe that freedom demands discipline.

At the time of writing a further twelve months have passed; he is doing well, coping with stresses as they arise without recourse to drugs of any sort. He has felt unsure of himself, he has felt like smoking hash, he has felt frustrated, angry and threatened, but he now realizes that most people get these feelings and he has allied himself to the 'Revolution of Purpose' that they share, offering a slow but real gain in emotional maturity and independence, rather than retreat from real problems into the false security of drug dependence.

Many of the problems common to the stories of young drug abusers are highlighted by the case of Peter—the progression from infrequent, almost casual, use to constant reliance on drugs to make life a softer, less frustrating experience. A great danger with cannabis is that it may remove the initial fears of using drugs. Peter was revolted by the sight of someone else 'mainlining hard drugs' yet, whilst under the influence of hashish, he thought that he might go on to try mainlining for a bigger kick. Fortunately for him, the time, situation or mood were never quite right for an impulsive fix; unfortunately for many others, they were.

A SMOKER TAKES A TRIP—ALEC

The Doors of Perception by Aldous Huxley, thirteen years ago, promised 'a world that human beings had never had before ... loving kindness, peace and joy ... visions of unimaginable richness and significance ... eons of blissful experience miraculously telescoped into a single hour ... human beings will be able to achieve effortlessly what in the past could only be achieved with difficulty by means of self-control and spiritual exercises'. Since then the door has been rather violently kicked in. Starting in the U.S.A., the cult of LSD and other psychedelic drugs has swept through Western society, often associated with 'hippies' (new to Britain but well established in the U.S.A. by 1957). In the extreme situation there is complete disengagement from organized society, as in the case of the Psychedelic League for Spiritual Discovery, whose slogan is 'Turn on, tune in, drop out'. That LSD trips are not always full of 'peace and joy' is often illustrated by reports published in the daily press. LSD (lysergic acid diethylamide 25) has been used by some psychiatrists in their treatment of mental illness, but it is reported that it can cause anxiety, agitation, depression, suicide, and temporary or longer-lasting mental disorder. A psychiatrist in California reports (August 1967) that he has treated a man who took LSD several times and became convinced that he was an orange. He locked himself in his room for fear that someone would touch him and he would turn into orange juice. He was regarded as totally and perhaps permanently psychotic. That the effects of this colourless, tasteless substance vary from person to person is now well known to its adherents; a 'bad trip' is spoken of, yet many, usually young people, are not deterred. The momentum seems to carry them along and we can expect other drugs of this type to appear with even more powerful hallucinogenic effects. In fact, other drugs such as DMT (dimethyltryptamine) and STP '(scientifically treated petroleum'—a substance which apparently resembles chemically both amphetamine and mescaline) have now started to get into the news. STP has had a dramatic effect and has already led to several deaths in California. Whereas, with LSD, a 'bad trip' can be cut short by giving drugs such as the phenothiazines, no such treatment is possible with an STP overdose; the effects of the substance are, in fact, enhanced by such treatment.

ALEC

Alec is a well built, intelligent young man of 21. He is the eldest of three children from his mother's first marriage, the parents having separated after a long period of vicious rows remembered even now most clearly by their children. His mother married again when Alec was 15, but he was never on good terms with his stepfather and remembers him chiefly for the occasions when he drank too much and threw his weight about. He was quite happy at grammar school, which he attended for seven years, being good at 'artistic' subjects and not very enthusiastic about mathematics and science.

On leaving school he found that work did not come at all naturally to him; the longest job he held was his first—five months in an office. From then on he went from job to job staying until he was bored or a self-contrived sacking enabled him to leave. He was rather quiet and shy in large groups but liked to mix with small groups of people. It was in such a small group that he met some like-minded youths and, with an unfriendly atmosphere at home and a low weekly income, he decided to join them on the road to easy money. This they did by shop and office breaking, at which they seem to have been quite successful. During this period Alec used part of his share of the loot to buy some hashish. He liked it and decided that he could go into business himself by buying in bulk and 'pushing' smaller quantities to others. He still lived at home in a London suburb and was soon smoking $3\frac{1}{2}$ ounces of hashish a week at £7 an ounce; to pay for it he broke down the ounces into small 'deals' selling them, at a large profit, both to regular customers and to chance users.

This pattern of living continued for three years. Sometimes he had jobs for short periods, but found it increasingly difficult to do anything. 'I became very jumpy; it took me a tremendous time to do a job and when I worked I did so very slowly. After 10 to 12 'joints' I got very tired. It also made me very hungry.' Now he did not even try to work but spent all his time smoking and pushing hashish.

Yet the early satisfaction he had derived from hash was waning. At a friend's suggestion he began taking LSD trips at 25s. a time. His mother who had suspected for a long time that he was using drugs, tried to discuss it with him one evening and he responded by leaving home and living in another part of London. This increased his need for money, but for a time it did not present much of a problem as he was now closer to his bigger customers. The next year, in terms of 'trips', was a world cruise. He began using LSD about twice a week, and four months later was using it every day, finally getting to the point where he was taking 'double trips' (twice the usual dose). From time to time he mixed with users of hard drugs, and experimented with heroin on three or four occasions.

'Some junkies gave it to me at a party in Kensington in order to try it out—they did not ask me to pay for it. I skin-popped but it did not do anything for me and I gave it up.'

This is a most interesting statement, for it illustrates that not all people who experiment with heroin necessarily become dependent on it, although they are probably a very small minority.

Suddenly his source of LSD dried up; he was also short of ready cash and things became intolerable. He visited several doctors in order to get some sleeping tablets and twice attempted suicide whilst in a depressed state a couple of days after an LSD trip. He also forged cheques to get money to buy more LSD and hashish but by now his financial needs were impossible to keep up with; before long he was apprehended by the police.

'Coming out of the LSD world has left me in a hell of a state; the world seemed so hostile, I had left behind everything that was magical and mystical. I had been lord of it all; if I wanted people to be small they were small, and if I wanted them to be large they were large. Everything I did was wonderful, music flowed out of the record player in colour. It was much better than the heightened perception I had known on hashish alone—I could *see* music. I never really had a bad trip; I did not feel anything I did not want to feel. My only complaint about LSD was that it did not last forever.'

He believes he must go to hospital in order to come to terms with himself, yet the memory clings tenaciously: 'Ordinary life as an ordinary person has no real attraction for me. I try to retain the wonderful phantasy life, the security of the LSD experience; it is so much more than reality.' Nevertheless, he does not believe that LSD should be freely available;'One cannot work on LSD ... the thought of work never occurred to me. On my first LSD trip the fact that I could walk was a revelation to me, it was mystical that I could put one foot in front of the other .. nobody in the world would do any work if everyone used LSD.'

It is interesting to contrast the views of the Latey Committee with those of many young persons today who cannot see any reason why they should or should not go on trips. They consider that it is for them to decide which to do and that the final decision is their own business.

6 Young Heroin and Cocaine Addicts

In 1959 the Home Office reported no addicts to dangerous drugs under 20 years of age; in the same year only 50 of the 454 (11%) known addicts were in the age bracket of 20 to 34. By 1966, this situation had changed dramatically; in the previous year (1965), of the 927 addicts to dangerous drugs, over half (42%) were under 35 years of age, and the overwhelming majority of these were taking heroin. Addiction, especially to heroin, was being recorded in increasing numbers in teenagers. A major question becomes, why did England have in the early 1960's an outbreak of youth addiction to drugs, especially heroin and cocaine?

THE CHANGING BRITISH SITUATION*

In the early 1960's it became apparent to some British observers that there was widespread use of marijuana and amphetamines, especially Purple Hearts, among the youth. A minority of these progressed to using heroin and cocaine and were soon found among the patient population in certain hospitals and institutions (see Chapter 2, p. 17).[1]

Becoming an addict follows a rather well-defined pattern which is illustrated in the case histories of Jim, Hans, and Igor, which are presented in this chapter. The process begins with the individual first buying Purple Hearts for such 'practical' reasons as staying awake for the entire week-end or to have more energy. Within a few months' time he is purchasing

---

* Adapted from M. M. Glatt (1966) A Review of the Second Report of the Interdepartmental Committee on Addiction. *Bull. Narcot.*, **18**, No. 2, 32.

marijuana cigarettes for smoking; both of these drugs are usually secured at a club or coffee bar, frequently in London's West End. Some youngsters, it should be noted, never progress in drugs beyond this stage. Perhaps for some of the psychologically more vulnerable, Purple Hearts and reefers are not sufficient for their needed kicks. They are introduced to heroin (and somewhat later to cocaine) by friends and acquaintances at parties and clubs and begin to take it for 'kicks', new experiences, or to find out what it is like. Their first heroin is usually obtained from a type of 'pseudo black market,' i.e. from addicts who obtain their supply from a prescribing general practitioner and manage to obtain a surplus which they sell to others at approximately £1 per grain (0·06 gram). These addict-pushers are what is meant by the term 'pseudo black market.'

In using heroin and cocaine the progression is typically from 'snorting' (sniffing through the nostrils), through 'skin-popping' (injecting underneath the skin), to 'mainlining' (direct injection into a vein). First, the youngster secures his supply from the black market, but as he becomes addicted his habit increases and becomes more expensive. To support himself and his habit he occasionally turns to criminal acts. This procedure is illustrated with the cases of Hans and Igor. More frequently, he becomes registered with one of the few doctors willing to prescribe for addicts; their names are generally well known among the addicts but not always, as the story from Hans illustrates. Often these registered addicts sooner or later sell part of their drug supply, thus introducing further teenagers to the use of heroin and cocaine.

It is hoped that the case histories of Jim, a registered addict, and Hans and Igor, non-registered addicts, will provide insight into why certain teenagers become addicted. Common elements occur in all three cases. On a psychological level, there was the absence of stable family life reflected in that they all come from broken homes. Male identification models were either not present or weak. Their adolescence has been marked by inadequate school and work performance and an almost goal-less orientation to life. Their pattern of adaptation to society is what the sociologists have frequently referred to as a retreatistic one, in which they 'opt out' of daily responsibilities, finding solace and comforts and kicks in a drug way of life.

JIM: A REGISTERED ADDICT

INTRODUCTION

Our first contact with Jim took place in 1965 when he was a patient at a psychiatric hospital where he was being treated for his addiction to heroin and cocaine. At the group meeting Jim participated in the discussion and afterwards we had a talk about his problem.

A young man of 22, Jim looked more youthful than this in his appearance. His hair was worn long in the fashion set by the pop singers. His 'gear' (clothes) were those made fashionable throughout the Western world by Carnaby Street, London, namely, bright shirt, wide tie, tight pants worn low on the hips with a wide belt. As is true with many youthful addicts, he evidenced a strong preoccupation with art, music, literature; in short, he viewed himself as being interested in the creative arts. He always had a book with him; several times when he was seen in the treatment unit he was asleep on his bed cradling a book.

Jim was eager to participate in this study, but when one of us interviewed him he was extremely nervous. He continually moved about, began to perspire profusely, and the pupils of his eyes dilated. It was difficult for him to stay focused on the subject under discussion, and at times it appeared that he had retreated into his special fantasy world.

FAMILY BACKGROUND

Jim was born in wartime England in the 1940's. His father was killed during the conflict, and his mother subsequently re-married. With his stepfather, a minor government official, and his mother he spent his childhood in India and West Africa, returning to England at age 16. His childhood appears to have been a lonely time, and his circle of friends was limited in these overseas posts. His interests in the arts and literature became dominant, and he entered a college to study art on his return. His stepfather left the family at the same time and Jim, at age 16, was launched into the outside world.

ADOLESCENCE AND DRUGS

At the age of 17, Jim was introduced in the Soho area of London to smoking marijuana at a private party which was attended

3*   65

almost exclusively by smokers and heroin users. He was not too aware of what effect to expect from marijuana, but it proved to be a pleasant experience which he continued over the next year. He obtained a job with an art gallery in London and continued to associate with the artistic crowd in Soho, especially actors.

By his 18th birthday, he had been introduced to heroin by a friend in the Soho area. One day the friend (already a user) came to the art gallery and asked Jim if he wanted to take some heroin; he readily consented to the friend's suggestion. From then until he was admitted to a hospital eight months later, he would take any kind of drug just for 'kicks'. After his initial 'cure' he stayed off drugs for a short period before relapsing.

From his 18th to 22nd birthday his absorption into the drug world became almost complete. He went from one prescribing doctor to another, particularly if they began to cut his dosage down. In this four-year period he was admitted to various hospitals five times for addiction cures. His record indicates that he attempted suicide at least four times. Even while hospitalized for his addiction he sometimes tried to continue taking drugs that he or his friends smuggled in. As an aside, it should be noted that this is a common problem for addiction treatment units for alcoholics and in particular for drug addicts—how to keep the environment free from alcohol and drug use.

Prior to becoming registered with a prescribing practitioner and after registration, Jim's drug intake generally always outran his supply. He had a criminal record of stealing, trying to sell a library book, and forging prescriptions (in the drug addict's argot, 'passing paper'). For example, he went to a practitioner, and while his back was turned he stole some prescription slips and altered them. His statement to the police was as follows: 'The expense for illegal pushers was too high; that's why I resorted to this' (altering the prescription blanks). He frequently became desperate for drugs and resorted to begging on the streets.

His work record throughout this four-year period was erratic, as might be expected. He sold few of the paintings which he completed, and he made copper jewellery for women, pendants, and leather thongs. It provided only partial support for his living expenses and drugs.

'REGISTRATION' AND REACTION TO DRUGS

A few months after becoming a heroin user Jim became registered' with Dr. A. He states, 'Well, at that time, I was using approximately 4 grains of heroin. I couldn't really pay for the heroin; it was getting too difficult to get money to get drugs, so I became registered with Dr. A. who cut me down. I was given 2 grains of heroin and 2 grains of cocaine instead of the 4 grains of heroin which I was using.' It should be noted that Jim, like most other drug addicts in England, was reluctant to become registered and put it off as long as possible. In his words, his attitude to being officially noted as a drug addict was : 'It's finally admitting sorta dependence upon the drug, you know; most people fight this thing down for so long, and then it's just got to happen, I suppose'. The negative attitude toward becoming registered on the part of the addict, as well as the unwillingness of most British doctors to prescribe heroin and cocaine, are points that some American observers find difficult to understand. These Americans frequently assume that addicts are desirous of becoming registered and that English practitioners are very willing to have addicts among their patient population (see Chapter 2). Neither assumption is valid.

Jim remained on Dr. A's patient list for approximately a year and was hospitalized to receive a 'cure'. For a few months he remained abstinent but he relapsed. He next found his way to Dr. B who was widely known for treating 'Canadians, jazz singers, and Americans with money', but he states he was not able to afford the cost of treatment provided by Dr. B and stopped seeing this doctor. He became very sick from the effects of drug withdrawal, and an addict friend took him to his practitioner, Dr. C, who registered him for 4 grains of heroin and 4 grains of cocaine, which was less than he was taking then. Jim reports that all of these three, Drs. A, B, and C, cut him down on his stated drug requirements.

Frequently Jim would receive a drug prescription which was to last him for three or four days, but he would 'blow it' (use it) in one day, or maybe one day and one night. This is a not unusual occurrence among addicts. Sometimes, after blowing his prescription, Jim would suffer. He states: 'Well, then you just shiver for a few days; you have to go out and hustle the drug or borrow it. This is when things get difficult, you know; it all comes down black and thick.'

At other times he would return to his doctor before another prescription was due with a concocted story of why he was short of drugs. He stated:

'It doesn't matter what story you tell the doctor; they still know you're short of the drug. They can tell you're short of the drug; maybe they will make up a prescription for half of your base supply for the next two days or something like that, or maybe cut down the "coc" (*cocaine*). . . . My usual story is that I took an overdose of cocaine and flushed the rest of the stuff down the toilet because I thought I was getting pretty close, you know, to the death one.'

Since Jim frequently blew his scrip, it was a constant battle to keep himself supplied with drugs. Financial resources to purchase drugs on the pseudo black market at £1 a grain were not always available, nor could he always give fabricated stories to explain his shortage to the prescribing practitioner. Occasionally, if he did not have the 'stuff' (drugs), he would 'fix up with Nembutal'. Jim commented, 'I would melt down 4 tablets and fix it up, fix it up warm because it congeals; you know that used to help me out, a little Nembutal.' But he would take almost anything to tide himself over until the next prescription was due.

Thus, at 22, Jim was constantly preoccupied with obtaining a 'fix' and getting the effect from the drugs. Although some addicts derive tremendous gratification from inserting the syringe needle (referred to as a 'spike') into the vein, Jim felt that he did not get much kick out of actually shooting it. For him, he states, 'It's just finding a vein and waiting for the flash. Then you can think about, well, you know, that was good. I made it!' With an injection of heroin and cocaine, he said, 'I felt as if I was going to fly. I tell you, it was hell.'

DEATH: THE FINAL KICK

Jim, prior to our talking with him, had made at least four suicidal attempts in the previous four years. In 1965, he was preoccupied with death and stated that he thought about it a lot. His description was: 'Death—that's the final kick'. He, however, did not know whether most addicts were preoccupied with death or not, but he was rather positive that they do not fear taking an overdose of drugs. In reference to this, he stated:

'You know I've been in the toilet where people are fixing, and they just suddenly fall down on the floor. (*He laughed nervously.*) A few of my friends have died from overdoses, but a few more have died from being taken off. It's not the drug that kills you, it's being taken off it, that's what really messes you up.'

Over the next few months Jim made several efforts to 'come off' drugs but relapsed almost immediately to the drug way of life. He re-registered with a general practitioner. Death—the final kick—came a few weeks later to Jim, allegedly from an overdose of heroin and cocaine.

'NON-REGISTERED' ADDICTS

A number of young people become addicted to drugs without ever having obtained drugs from a doctor. This access to the pseudo black market occurs through drugs being sold by registered addicts to their 'friends'. Some might question whether these individuals are really friends—some must engage in pushing drugs to supplement their income, since addiction is not really compatible with all the responsibilities that go with holding a job, especially in the youth period.

To pay for these illicit drugs the individual may even resort to petty crime—shoplifting, pilfering, and occasionally prostitution, heterosexual or homosexual. Furthermore, 'passing paper' (forging prescriptions) is a not uncommon occurrence.

The following case of Hans illustrates the non-registered addict who frequently gets into difficulty with family and police authorities over his drug habits; his criminality frequently leads to a prison term.

HANS: 'A NON-REGISTERED ADDICT'

Hans was born in 1947 in an English provincial town. As the only child, he was indulged by his mother in almost every way. When he was 3 years old, his father died but his mother did not remarry for twelve years.

Occasionally, as a child, he had difficulty with bladder control, being enuretic. The mother stated that because of his nervousness she thought of taking him to a psychiatrist when he was only 8 years of age but she never got around to making an appointment. In school, which he attended from his 5th to 15th year, he was rated as average.

Leaving school, he became an apprentice construction worker and apparently did quite well, but after two-and-a-half years he left to become an automobile mechanic; this last position he held only for nine months because he frequently had to take time off from work because he had started to take large numbers of Purple Hearts. His occupational adjustment after this firing was marginal; he worked for a short period of time as a storekeeper, but because of his drug taking he was frequently sick and was unable to work regularly. Thus, occupational deterioration set in before he was 19 years of age.

The psychiatrist who examined him described Hans as basically of sound personality structure, one who is not psychopathic or antisocial. Furthermore, his attitude to sex was apparently normal, and he had a number of girl friends. Hans describes himself as a good mixer, a happy-go-lucky person who takes things in his stride, and a good hard worker until he began to take pills.

His adjustment as a teenager to his family, from the record, appears to be more problematic. Shortly after his 16th birthday he left home because he wanted more freedom. His mother was extremely religious, and his recently acquired stepfather was only slightly less so. Also, he felt that his stepfather was jealous of him. His mother objected to his going out with friends drinking; to circumvent this, he visited a friend in London for a week becoming introduced to the beatniks, the Campaign for Nuclear Disarmament, and, in short, a new set of values.

DRUG HISTORY

Three years ago, at 16 years of age, Hans started to take Drinamyl or Purple Hearts with an initial intake of 5 pills a day, which he quickly built up to 20 daily, paying on the black market at that time 6*d* for each one. His stated motivation for taking pills was that he wanted to have more energy for his cycling. Most of the Purple Hearts were obtained in the clubs and coffee bars in his home town in the Midlands, which he frequented because most of his friends went there. He states, 'I got into the wrong company, beatniks, and the majority of them were out of work and stealing'. Pep pills made him feel lively, full of energy, and light-headed. Simultaneously he experimented with Dexedrine and Benzedrine.

About six months after beginning to take amphetamines, he had his first experience with smoking marijuana, which he obtained in a club he frequented in the Midlands. The black market price at this time was £6 per ounce of marijuana. In his words, he smoked 'a hell of a lot' with two or three friends in their flat. He described the effect of the smoking as being similar to being intoxicated. He stated:

'I felt dizzy, very, very happy, and giddy; it felt a bit like being drunk, but was better than getting drunk. Colours seemed to be more vivid; they seemed to stand out more. I used it to appreciate music better.'

And later:

'I used to see things. I used to imagine small people walking about in front of me. I was under the influence of marijuana so much that I didn't get scared by this vision. I was too stoned.'

After his 18th birthday, or approximately two-and-a-half years after beginning to take Purple Hearts and later smoking marijuana, he escalated to using heroin and cocaine. Occasionally he came to London to visit friends and while at one of the clubs in the West End he met a number of 'registered junkies'. They told him that taking heroin was better than marijuana. For his first connection he paid £1 per grain, although his usual price was 10s to 15s per grain. Occasionally, over a period of four months he took heroin, and 4 grains would last him a fortnight. Signs of addiction to heroin began to appear in the form of an abstinence syndrome when he ran out of his supply at his home in the Midlands. He states, 'I felt sick, had stomach cramps, the horrors, the ceilings were falling, and it was horrible; so I went to London and bought some more'.

When he started taking heroin, he did 'skin-popping' with a needle attached to the end of an eyedropper with cellophane tape. He used the eyedropper—after breaking his syringe—because it was cheaper this way. He denies that he ever did any 'snorting'. Later he only mainlined heroin and cocaine. About two months after using heroin he started on cocaine because he was told that it was a stimulant; he felt tired from heroin only and wanted to keep awake.

After beginning to use heroin and cocaine he had to take

more and more time off from work, although this had not been so when he was using amphetamines and smoking marijuana. He could not face getting up in the mornings, so he stayed in bed, not going to work. Even when working he had to go to the toilet to fix two or three times a day. It would take him about half an hour each time as he was fumbling with a teaspoon and syringe, and he was anxious about the amount of time he was taking.

After about two weeks of using heroin Hans became addicted, although he was not taking more than 1 grain per day. He exhibited the classic symptoms which have been previously described. He attempted to become registered through his family doctor in the Midlands and was refused; a number of other practitioners in his home town and London also refused to prescribe drugs for him. His experience in trying to get the names of prescribing doctors from 'registered junkies' is interesting, because it is generally stated that these heroin users have a code of ethics which dictates that they help each other. In Hans's story this is not so. He states that fellow addicts refused to give him the names of their doctors so he could register with them. These addicts stated that it was useless to ask their doctor as he was too busy to prescribe; thus, he never did obtain the name of a doctor who would prescribe drugs to him.

To support his drug habit he began to steal, engaging in shoplifting about twice a week. He maintains that he never pushed any heroin or cocaine himself, that he was only a purchaser. Eventually, he was arrested by the police for stealing and sentenced to a term in prison. At the time he was arrested he was taking 5 grains of heroin and 3 grains of cocaine a day, and he had taken as much as 7 grains of heroin and 4 grains of cocaine. Asked whether he thought heroin or cocaine was more likely to produce strong dependence, he responded that heroin is the more addictive of the two and that he had never met a pure cocaine addict. His heroin and cocaine were always exclusively obtained from registered addicts. He says he knows about 20 registered junkies as against 7 non-registered addicts, as well as about 7 or 8 people who take heroin or cocaine for kicks. These latter individuals come to town mainly on week-ends and perhaps take 1 grain of heroin over the entire week-end. 'Maybe', he says, 'they only take it to show off in front of registered junkies.'

DRUGS AND PERSONALITY CHANGE

Hans, in his quest for independence and identity, moved from his parental home at an early age—shortly after his 16th birthday. This coupled with early leaving of school at 15 and entering into the labour force, launched him into society before social and psychological maturity had been achieved. He found his way to the permissive drug-taking environment of the clubs and coffee bars, frequented by the beatniks and other rootless individuals of society. Perhaps seeking identification with a larger organization he joined a group interested in nuclear disarmament, where he says he also met people who took drugs and sometimes passed out reefers without payment.

His mother notes that his personality began to change after this and he himself states that he started arguments with his parents, that he became bad tempered, and had depressive moods. His arm became swollen and infected from drug injections. Before taking drugs, his mother states he never used to steal or lie, but he explains this by saying, 'I had to steal as I couldn't afford to buy the drugs otherwise'. His mother even went to the police about Hans's drug taking, but they maintained they could not do anything unless drugs were found on him.

In conclusion, Hans feels that his search for freedom and his drug taking may be a reaction to his having been brought up very strictly by his mother and from his being required to go regularly to Sunday School. Whether his perceptions are valid from a strictly scientific point is another question, but this is the way he defines the situation of his having become a drug addict, and this is meaningful in his being treated for his problem.

IGOR: QUEST FOR IDENTITY

At 18 years of age, Igor, a male born in London, is well indoctrinated into the subculture of drug addiction, despite the fact that he has never legally secured drugs from a prescribing doctor. He has progressed from smoking marijuana to becoming a heroin addict in little more than two years. To obtain his drug supply from the pseudo black market he has engaged in an extensive life of crime to secure the necessary financial resources. Most recently, he has served a prison term for stealing cars which were sold to support his drug habit.

The family background of this youngster provided the fertile soil in which drug dependence could develop. Prior to taking drugs he was evidencing problems with authority and had difficulty remaining in school and later in holding down a job.

FAMILY BACKGROUND

Born in the late 1940's in a middle-class area of London, he was the illegitimate son of an artist with whom his mother, a medical technician, was having an affair. His 'biological' father refused to marry his mother, absconded to Canada, and the mother, shortly before Igor's birth, married a dental student. He was viewed as being the oldest of four children who were a product of this marriage. When he was 7 years of age, his mother divorced his legal father, and the mother informed Igor at the same time that he was illegitimate. To Igor, it always seemed different at home after this fact was revealed to him.

Three years later, when Igor was 10, his mother married a business executive. This stepfather is good to him, Igor feels, but this man has never really put himself out for him. His childhood was marked by many neurotic traits such as thumb sucking, nail biting, and nightmares. Both at nursery and primary schools he cried a great deal—especially whenever he left his mother's house.

His relationship to his parental figures are fraught with ambivalences. Of his mother he states, 'I always blame my mother for everything that has gone wrong, but she has always, nevertheless, been the first person I come to when in trouble, though I'm very rude to her'. As far as can be determined, there has been no contact with his biological father, the artist. Toward his legal father, he feels that he owed him (Igor) something. For example, despite this man's wealth, he never had a chance to go to an exclusive school. Thus Igor states: 'I always felt that if things went too bad, I would be able to get money from my legal father. I look exactly like my father's other legitimate son whom I happened to come across recently. I feel bitter about that.' His stepfather, whom he now sees only occasionally, is also the object of mixed feelings. Although the relationship with him is not close, the stepfather has supported him when he has been expelled from schools and when he has been out of work. In short, Igor feels that his mother has cheated him out of a father, and for this reason he has a basic feeling of insecurity.

SCHOOL AND ADOLESCENCE

Igor's school adjustment was always problematic, from his entry in school at 5 to his being expelled at 15 years of age for being truant. At school he was interested in history, art, and English, but he states:

'I never did any work at school. All sorts of things used to put me off. For instance, taking days off and getting way behind in my work. I never had much to do with other boys at school, but I had different friends at home. I didn't get on well with most of the teachers. I always got the cane, at first being ashamed of it, but later was boasting about it.'

Despite his being expelled from school at 15, his parents got him enrolled in a technical college at age 16, after he had spent one year working as an apprentice. He lasted in the college shortly over a year before being expelled for smoking marijuana.

His difficulty with the police began early; at 13 years of age he was arrested for shoplifting records. At 17 he was apprehended for driving without a licence, and most recently for stealing automobiles. He states in reference to the last offence

'It never affected my conscience to take away cars. I didn't care about the particular person who owned the car. I just had to sell it to get some money to buy drugs. Anyway, it's the insurance that pays for the cars and so these people don't really lose anything.'

Igor, on the whole, has good insight into his personality makeup, describing himself basically as a drifting, goal-less adolescent. Of himself he states:

'I never have been able to concentrate on anything in my life. I always felt that by staying indoors I might miss something in my life. If I ever got interested in anything, it soon wore off. But having fun, going to parties, and so on, that was not boring.'

But he has a realistic appraisal of his situation at 18 years of age. He declares:

'I can't even keep a job. I've always messed about at school. I had numerous chances. I have an inferiority complex. I've always been afraid of having girl friends unless I had drugs.'

INTRODUCTION TO DRUGS: MARIJUANA

Igor was introduced to marijuana at 16 years of age by a girl friend when he was a student at the London technical college. There is evidence that he had previously experimented with taking Purple Hearts and Dexedrine and had been intoxicated from alcoholic beverages several times. He states that the majority of his friends used to drink before they got onto the 'pot' (marijuana) spree. Most of the group took pot for only a short while as a novelty or a desire for a new experience. In his words, 'They just wanted to try it out for kicks, just like getting in bed with a girl'.

Whatever the original motivations for his smoking marijuana, it became a very gratifying experience for him. His psychological rewards from smoking are expressed as follows:

'When you first smoke it, you feel great. It is a marvellous experience. You look forward to smoking it, to things connected with it; for instance, to the finding of a place where you can smoke it....With marijuana, you can't be bothered. For instance, at a dance you don't want to get up to take a pretty girl for a dance. When there is a non-smoker at the party that ruins it. We can't stand having anybody there not smoking like we smoke. You like to be there at parties with people just looking at it, this marijuana; you feel that people are looking at you. You think you capture a person's personality that's smoking.'

Given this social psychological fixation on the magical powers of marijuana for the individual, it is doubtful that Igor will stop smoking reefers. Buttressing this is his statement that everything else in his life had failed, and Igor wanted to impress others.

The secrecy and undercover work necessary to obtain marijuana probably increases the adolescent's attraction for the drug. His group would buy 2 or 3 ounces of marijuana at a time, out of which they would make many cigarettes. Once (in a club) a man cheated him out of £7 he had given him to get marijuana. He never gave the risk of being caught a second thought when smoking reefers. When he realized that he had to have money for drugs, he states that 'It made the task of our having to take a car easier as we knew we just had to have the money'.

FROM MARIJUANA TO HEROIN

Igor indicates that he was more afraid of having his first marijuana than his first heroin injection, which occurred approximately fifteen months later. His mother, the medical technician, had warned him to stay off drugs. Perhaps he had been afraid of becoming addicted to marijuana, and when that did not occur, he was less scared of taking heroin.

His first experience with heroin occurred almost accidentally, although we would conjecture that it was perhaps inevitable, given his pattern of life at this time, despite his protestations that up to this point he had avoided 'taking the plunge' (using heroin). He describes the occasion as follows:

'I couldn't get marijuana that day. Rather than go back empty-handed to my two friends, who waited for me to bring them marijuana, I bought 3 grains of heroin for which I paid £3 10s. One friend was apprehensive, rather than taking the heroin found himself a girl friend and went out. So it left only this other chap and me. So we took the plunge.'

As with marijuana, he obtained great satisfaction from heroin. He describes the effect as follows:

'When you try one thing, you feel good; there's nothing like it. It's like a dream, it's fantastic, like with heroin. If you feel you like it, you don't want to stop, but if you want to stop, it means giving up all your old friends with the same interest.'

Today he feels he took the plunge because of an inferiority complex, especially with girls, and also because it seemed romantic to be an American hipster. He wanted to be like certain jazz musicians who are known to be users of marijuana and heroin.

He became addicted to heroin within a short period of time. At parties he and friends began their experience with cocaine by sniffing it through the nostrils. Gradually his habit with heroin increased to 8 grains a day plus cocaine now and then. This is an expensive habit to support. Where did he get the supply? Although he knew that he could become registered with a prescribing practitioner, he was extremely afraid that his mother would find out, and he did not want her to know.

To support his habit by obtaining drugs from registered addicts and from those to whom it had been sold by these addicts, he turned to criminal behaviour. Occasionally he broke into chemist shops and doctors' offices, stealing all kinds of tablets and prescription blanks. He also stole to obtain money for heroin, but Igor always seemed to be in tremendous debt. His major criminal activity was stealing cars. He says:

' At first we took the cars for fun, to run away from the police and to have excitement. But later I was taking cars for the sheer necessity of supporting my habit. . . . One week I sold about four cars, and I made £10 to £40 on each.'

He would do almost anything to obtain money. 'Sometimes', he said, 'I would never dream of doing something such as a homosexual act, but I would wind up doing it for money.' On another occasion, Igor and his friends committed robbery with violence when they did not have any money. He relates, 'We walked about thinking about attacking somebody. We waylaid a middle-aged homosexual, hit him five times with a rock until he gave us his wallet with £30.' For this offence he was never apprehended.

THE FUTURE

While incarcerated in prison, drugs posed no problem for Igor. His orientation to drugs when he was released from prison can be summarized in his own words, 'I would rather not go back on hard drugs (*heroin and cocaine*), but I want to go on smoking (*marijuana*)'. This is not an infrequent statement among these youngsters. Indoctrinated into the drug subculture, they find it difficult to make a complete break with it, actually holding tenaciously onto the idea that they can smoke. But rarely is smoking an isolated act carried on in privacy. It is usually a group experience which attracts other drug users and carries in this context a whole set of attitudes and values; in short, a way of life in which a number will progress from smoking to mainlining.

The gratification that smokers receive from marijuana is difficult for non-users to realize. For example, Igor states that 'marijuana is definitely habit forming'; he is always looking forward to it. He has wanted to stop and he could not, for he says, 'I look forward to smoking every evening'.

Admittedly, the prognosis for Igor is problematic. At 18 he is without job and educational skills and experiences; he is confused about his family situation and his relationships to his mother and series of fathers. Furthermore, he has unresolved problems with his sexual identity. His experience with drugs is extensive. He has taken Purple Hearts and Dexedrine, and at one time even smoked opium. Of this experience, he comments:

'Opium makes you feel more at ease, but much more sluggish. You feel like sitting down and not moving. With heroin, on the other hand, you could move and dance.'

On the other hand, despite his criminal offences and having been incarcerated, his positive valences are toward the use of drugs, especially smoking marijuana. For, as he states, 'When I'm smoking reefers, I'm not so aware of things'.

And perhaps this is the key to his drug problem!

REFERENCE

1. Glatt, M. M. (1965) Reflections on Heroin and Cocaine Addiction. *Lancet*, **ii**, 171.

7 Recovered Addicts

Until a few years ago the problem of drug dependence in Britain chiefly affected the middle-aged women, such as harassed housewives who, in an effort to find relief from anxiety and tension or from the intolerable burden of overwork, had asked their doctor for help. Tranquillizers were then not available, so that the practitioner tended to fall back on his old allies and standbys, i.e. barbiturates and, since the late 1940's, amphetamines. The latter, moreover, were widely prescribed in order to curb the appetite of women who wanted to slim. The fact (stressed by Willcox as long ago as the late twenties and early thirties) of barbiturates being addictive drugs was not generally accepted, as he seemed to have lost 'The Battle of the Barbiturates', fought out in the early thirties in the columns of *The Lancet* and in heated discussions and arguments at meetings of London's medical societies. As regards amphetamines, it only became known in the 1950's that they could in fact lead to habituation—i.e. psychological dependence—apart from other risks such as that of a paranoid psychosis (fortunately reversible) clinically indistinguishable from paranoid schizophrenia. Thus, beginning in the early 1950's, one began to see individuals dependent on barbiturates and amphetamines; and this condition was not uncommon also in alcoholics who, when put on barbiturates by their doctors in an effort to free them from alcohol, often found that these drugs could do for them what alcohol did—and often more rapidly and much more cheaply. Only rarely did one come across the occasional 'therapeutic' or 'professional' morphine or pethidine addicts—people who had become addicted when being treated with these drugs for one of the few conditions which constitute legitimate indications for prescribing them; or, on the other hand, members of the 'healing' professions, such as doctors, nurses, pharmacists, who have easy, constant access to the 'Dangerous Drugs', and thus have a greater opportunity and a greater risk of addiction than the average citizen, less often exposed to the opportunity and temptation.

This type of therapeutic and professional addict has in recent years become proportionately and progressively less common, his place having been taken more and more by the new wave of addicts; new, that is, as far as this country is concerned: the young heroin–cocaine addicts. They present in many respects a new proposition, a new challenge, and neither State nor the medical profession are prepared for their arrival. Consequently no adequate treatment arrange-ments are available, no provision has been made for proper after-care, and hardly anybody has any experience in treating this type of addict. If one adds to this the fact that little is known as to the cause of this form of drug dependence, or as to the precipitating and contributing factors, quite apart from the type of personality involved, it is small wonder that results of treatment are, unfortunately, still highly unsatisfactory. They are certainly worse than in the case of the professional or therapeutic barbiturate addict mentioned above whose per-sonal stability may be expected to be higher than that of the average new heroin and cocaine addict. After all, the former acquired his dependence in a semi-legitimate way, whereas the new addict had to go out of his way to acquire the drugs in an illegal manner. However, as we have seen, the latter is not strictly true as, under the British system, medical practitioners could quite legitimately prescribe these drugs for individuals whom they felt to be in need of them.

The first Report of the Interdepartmental Committee in 1961[1] had a great deal to say about the 'stabilized addict', i.e. a person who was able to maintain a fixed dose of the narcotic drug without the need for ever-increasing doses and who, at the same time, was able to follow his occupation. The Com-mittee gave a number of case histories of 'stabilized addicts'; but all were examples of middle-aged, therapeutic addicts who had little in common with the new young heroin and cocaine addicts. Most observers have only rarely come across such stabilized addicts; the majority of heroin–cocaine addicts— especially the cocaine addicts whom one sees—are quite unable to follow their occupation regularly. One young addict's terse comment was: 'Addicts do not work!' although it appears that some jazz musicians are able to do so for varying periods of time. Certain 'prescribing' doctors maintain that some of their patients do in fact work fairly steadily and regularly, but the likelihood is that these, too, are mostly therapeutic addicts and not the new young variety.

Thus, the prognosis for the new addicted youngsters by-and-large must be considered as generally worse than among the older therapeutic addict. Most of the young addicts treated at the St. Bernard's Hospital Drug Dependence Unit relapsed fairly soon after discharge. However, from time to time one saw pleasant surprises—the more surprising as only make-shift arrangements could be made for their treatment in those days, and after-care facilities were virtually absent. One example of a student who had become emotionally dependent on hashish and who now, one-and-a-half years after discharge, is still free from drugs, has resumed work at university and is doing well in every respect, was given in Chapter 5. The following are examples of two 'recovered' heroin addicts.

CASE I

Although the exact influence of the influx of Canadian* and American addicts on the British drug scene cannot be assessed there is little doubt that their arrival in this country in the early 1960's must have helped to arouse interest in drug taking in suggestible youngsters who had money in their pockets, time on their hands, and were yearning for a break from monotonous boredom. These 'refugees' from the oppressive drug laws in their homeland—where addiction was regarded as a punishable crime and not, as in Britain, as a disease which should be treated—had often spent years in jail. They had learnt of the possibility of being able to get drugs quite legitimately in this country without being hunted by the police. As a rule, even before arrival, they had been given names of doctors willing and prepared to prescribe for them. Ed is a case in point. He is a Canadian who became addicted to heroin when 16 years old in Toronto. He came to Britain in 1961 after serving several prison terms in Canada. He had, in fact, spent four of the preceding five years in jail. When arriving in Britain

* The lot of the majority of these Canadian addicts was not very happy. Some five years ago a London practitioner published results which were on the whole promising. However, Home Office files show that by 1967 many had relapsed, and some had been deported to Canada. On the other hand, apart from the addicts described in this chapter, two further Canadian ex-patients of St. Bernard's Hospital, whose permanent abstinence seemed anything but promising, have in fact been able to keep away from drugs for over a year now.

he went straight to a private practitioner whose name he had been given in Canada; after obtaining drugs for a time from this doctor he tried his luck with a National Health Service practitioner. He was indeed in luck; this doctor took him on. (The great majority of doctors in Britain fought shy of taking addicts on their list, and most addicts had great difficulty in finding doctors willing to prescribe, apart from the few (well known to most London addicts) who had relatively large numbers of addicts on their lists. Addicts coming from the provinces often had great difficulty in finding doctors who would prescribe for them (cf. Chapter 6).)

The following is a transcript of an interview conducted with Ed:

Question: When did you come to England?

Ed: In the Spring of 1962.

Question: How long have you been an addict?

Ed: Nine years.

Question: Were you still taking drugs when you arrived in England?

Ed: No. I had just been released from the penitentiary.

Question: What was your idea in coming to England?

Ed: To further my addiction without having to land in jail; to keep out of jail.

Question: When coming over, how long was it before you started taking drugs again after landing?

Ed: The same day that I landed.

Question: Where did you get these drugs?

Ed: From Dr. X. I knew about this doctor before I came over. I knew of several doctors.

Question: Was this commonly known in Canada amongst the addicts?

Ed: Well, it was in my section of Canada.

Question: Did you have any trouble getting drugs from this doctor?

Ed: None whatsoever. No, I got what I asked for.

Question: Could you describe what went on on the day you first attended this doctor?

Ed: I told this doctor that I had just arrived from Canada; that I was addicted—i.e. that I was still taking drugs—which was not really true as I was not taking any at the time. I said I was using 4 grains of heroin a day and that if possible I would like to go on the books as a 'registered' addict; and the doctor said: 'Certainly'.

Question: How much were you charged?

Ed: Well, there was no set charge ... whatever you could afford at the time ... one guinea to two guineas, plus the charge for your drugs.

Question: Do you know any other Canadian addicts over here?

Ed: I know quite a few. There must have been 25 at the time I came over here.

Question: How old were you when you came over?

Ed: Twenty-two.

Question: Did you hang around with these other addicts very much?

Ed: No, very seldom ... I was working some of the time.

Question: Did you ever go to the West End, Soho, Paddington or Battersea?

Ed: Oh yes, I knew all the ins and outs of the addicts and where the addicts mix in England.

Question: Did you smoke any weed while you were over here, or take any Purple Hearts?

Ed: No, I am just a heroin addict. (*We heard from a number of Canadian heroin addicts who had never before taken cocaine that they started on cocaine after arrival here; when asked by the doctor whether they had been on cocaine, they answered:' Yes'. As there seemed to be a 'kick' in store for them for the asking, they didn't see why they should say:' No'.*)

Question: When you got over here, did you find any difference between the typical English addict and the typical Canadian addict?

Ed: Oh, there's a lot of difference. The addict back home is always on the look-out for police, having to steal all day long to get money for the drugs. Here if you couldn't afford the drugs privately you could get them under the N.H.S. If you were a 'registered' addict you never needed to have any fear about the police—in all my time here I have never been stopped by the police once—whether you were in town or out of town.

There are other differences, too. As regards dress, the English addict is a lot scruffier. It seems that because he has easier access to drugs he lets himself go far beyond the American addict.

Question: What do you think about the type of person who becomes an addict in Britain compared to Canada? Do you think there is a difference there?

Ed: They are quite different. In North America addicts are mainly concerned with stealing all day long; this is the main topic of conversation. In England an addict knows he is going to get his prescribed dosage; he accepts it and acts accordingly ... it's pretty hard to describe.

Question: Did you ever sell drugs or give drugs to other addicts or other users when you first started on the 4 grains prescribed for you?

Ed: No, I never did. I always used my prescribed dosage. (*This is the stock answer usually given at first interview: as a rule these people later admit to selling drugs (cf. p. 21). The temptation to make an easy 20s per grain must be very strong, the more so as addicts rarely work and may live on National Assistance, etc. Often these addicts try to draw a clear line between selling some stuff to friends in need of a 'fix', and 'pushing' larger quantities of the drug. See also Chapter 2.)*

Question: Do you think other Canadian addicts sold drugs?

Ed: Well, I don't know many who did, but I did know some who got so much from their doctors that they didn't need, so they sold it.

Question: Do you know whether they were selling to other addicts or to non-users?

Ed: To other addicts as far as I know. I was not really interested in it because I was not concerned as long as I got the prescription.

Question: Were there any clubs or areas in London where the Canadians were more concentrated than in other areas?

Ed: At the time they were concentrated not in Soho but in *X* Street, which is near to the place where my doctor has the practice.

Question: Do they keep to themselves very much?

Ed: You know addicts always stick together. Any outsiders were just simply 'squares'.

Question: Did they mix very much with the British addicts?

Ed: No, they did not feel they had anything in common, a sort of feeling superior. The Canadian addict had been through so much and he had seen so much, been in jail dozens of times, whereas the British addict might be at it for years and never been in jail. It is an entirely different outlook, snobbery.

Question: You said that you went to the West End addicts' hangouts. Were these places very different from the places addicts went to in Canada? Was it a different type of atmosphere?

Ed: Altogether! Whereas in this country addicts might habituate a place and be there all day, in Canada they were lucky if they were in a place for one hour, they always had to keep moving as police were breaking down the doors and what not...

Question: About now, having been completely off drugs for several years, you can start looking at the drug scene from outside. Do you think there has been any change in the type of British individual who has started taking drugs? One sees newspaper articles about 14- or 15-year-olds being addicted. Did you find this was the case when you were addicted?

Ed: No, the majority of people seemed to be a bit older at the time. I was not exactly an old man myself, but teenagers are at it today. I think it may be due to their being able to get hold of Purple Hearts, and to being able to smoke reefers which are coming into this country, and this may be the reason why addicts today may be even younger... Back in Canada if a young addict starts drugs he is always passing it on to his friends, and in this way personal influence does breed addiction.

Question: Did you find any cases of addicts who stole to get money for the black market in Britain, or steal to pay for their scrip?

Ed: Well, I only knew of one Canadian and he got deported for it... But then I did not mix much with other addicts; at the time I was working, I just wanted to use drugs and be left alone. I made my own acquaintances with people who weren't using drugs. Thus I did not know much about other addicts.

Question: How typical do you think you are in this pattern of most addicts who came over?

Ed: I think that at the time there were about 25 Canadian addicts in England and then they began to stop them coming over. I think that almost all have been deported by now. I have not seen a Canadian addict for two years, so I could not really say.

Question: Why were they deported?

Ed: The majority of them for petty crimes or forging prescriptions, or something.

Question: Those who were deported, had they mixed with the British addicts?

Ed: Yes, I believe they did.

Question: Were you surprised when you came over here to find the use of the same type of jargon, the same type of phrases that Canadian and American addicts use?

Ed: Entirely different at the time I came over in 1962. Our own way of phrasing things . . . we had a jail slang in relation to drugs. . . . The English addict seemed very 'square' to us . . . I am being told now that the British and the American terminology are very similar, but I don't know. I did not really have much to do with addicts so I could not truthfully tell. I did not want to know anybody socially or 'anti-socially' if you would like to call it, I wanted to be a junkie my own way. I did not want to mix with addicts and that is why I saw other people who were not using drugs. I think that is one of the basic reasons why I did manage to come off drugs.

Question: Let us talk now as to how you came off. Can you explain why you did come off?

Ed: Well, I think that it comes down to the fact that I reached saturation point. I had gradually stepped up to using 12 grains of heroin a day, as well as 8 grains of cocaine—all of which I was getting quite legally by then from a N.H.S. doctor. Finally, it came to the point where I could not work any more, and I was a walking zombie . . . I had been thinking for six months about going to hospital, until finally one day I found I was 'fixing' myself every hour or two and the needle was continually going in and out. I just could not stand it any longer, I could not live with myself.

Question: At the time, then, you were no longer attending your first doctor?

Ed: No, I had switched doctors. I could not get the dosage I wanted, so I went looking for another doctor and I found one in four months. He gave me whatever I asked.

Question: How did you pay for your habit when you were out of work and on this huge dosage?

Ed: Well, I did resort to stealing a couple of times; the majority (*of time*) I was just bumming around. I got money periodically from home, living on relief, any way I could, nothing really bad because I did not have the heart to go on stealing any more and wind up once more going to jail.

Question : When you first went to your second doctor did he question you about your dosage or anything ?

Ed : No, when I first went to see him I gave him a hard luck story— which all addicts are able to sell, having done it so often, although all junkie doctors must have heard them hundreds of times—which every addict is fully equipped with, and told him, quite untruthfully, that I was using 12 grains—and he give it to me straight away. There was no hesitation whatsoever.... He did not inquire any further— he knew I was with the other doctor at the time, and he told me to sever relationships there before he could deal with me—and that was all it amounted to. He never contacted my first doctor at all.

Question : He did not have much of an addicts' clientele at the time ?

Ed : No, I think I was the first one on his books—I think I originally 'discovered' him.

Question : What year was that?

Ed : 1962. A year later I went to see a psychiatrist in a London out-patient clinic who sent me to hospital. I stayed in hospital for three months and started to work outside a few weeks before actually leaving hospital. I had no drugs whatsoever since that time. I have worked steadily and got promoted. I have married and have two children. I have been able to save money and I am paying the mortgage on my home. I am very happy and contented. (*When he was interviewed again about one-and-a-half years later he had continued to make steady progress, looking smart, well-dressed and happy.*)

Question : How old were you when entering hospital?

Ed : Twenty-three.

Question : And how long, and how severely, had you been addicted at the time ?

Ed : I started to take drugs when I was 14 years old in Canada. I did it out of curiosity having met some teenage drug addicts at a party and when a friend asked me to have a 'fix'. At first I 'fixed' only once a week, then more often, and after about six months I was addicted. I was put in jail three times. I felt very hostile about that and hostile to society in general. I got into a state where I wanted to fix every hour because I could not accept responsibility and whenever I was confronted by anything that might be a bit unpleasant ... I left school at about 16, and afterwards I never held a job for longer than a few weeks; I could not settle down. In order to be able to buy heroin I had to steal quite a bit, mainly shoplifting. When aged 17, I was in prison for one year for being in possession of narcotics. I was very resentful about that, and within a fortnight of coming out of prison I was charged again, and again put into prison, this time for two years, from 1958 to 1960. On a third occasion I was charged with theft, and put back into prison for another six months. I came out in November 1960. I then tried to pull myself together; I left the city and took up a job in the country on building work. I managed to stay off drugs for a year but then I decided to go back to the city. Here I met again with addicts; I went back on drugs and by the end of 1961 I was again addicted. As it became a criminal offence in Canada to be a drug addict and I was well known to the police over there, and under some surveillance, I decided to come over to England. About a year later I entered hospital.

(Before coming over to this country he had been on about 3 grains daily but gradually he increased the dose, receiving for the six months before hospital admission 12 grains on doctor's prescription. In hospital he was withdrawn gradually, the heroin being replaced by methadone; the withdrawal period was uneventful, and within a fortnight he was off narcotics. He was a co-operative patient throughout except on one occasion three weeks after admission when he returned to the ward under the influence of alcohol. At the time he stated that on a previous occasion he had gone home, where he had destroyed his supply of heroin, amounting to 400 (gr. 1/6th) heroin tablets and broken his syringe. In the ward—where the majority of patients were alcoholics, with a few addicts —he proved very helpful, attended group therapy sessions, and was chosen deputy group leader by the group. After a stay of roughly three months he found himself a job and left hospital about a week later. He keeps in regular contact with the hospital staff, coming to hospital for occasional visits. He comes to group meetings to discuss matters with other addicts whenever asked to do so, and has been of great help during postgraduate medical courses, talking freely about his experiences and answering any questions put to him by doctors attending these meetings.)

Question : What do you think, in retrospect, were the factors helping you over the past three-and-a-half years to keep off drugs?

Ed : To start with, getting a job whilst still in hospital, and staying on there for a while whilst working outside, helped a great deal. Thus I found new friends—people who were not fixing—straight away. I think this is very important. Whenever I felt like a fix I tried to have people around me who did not fix and whom I liked; if you do not do anything to help yourself at the time you begin to think of the past and you will go back to fixing ... I cut myself off completely from the old environment as it is so easy to get fixes. There are as many places where you get fixes as there are pubs for drinking.... It is always the same; going down to your old crowd merely for a chit-chat with the boys, and before you know where you are you have a fix.... I have found that living with people is much easier than fighting them!

At a group meeting in the hospital which Ed attended recently some newly admitted young addicts questioned him about his views and recent attitudes—regular, steady work, home, family, etc. Their somewhat critical and doubting questions prompted Ed to the counter-question: 'Do addicts regard it as a crime to conform?' In some ways this is similar to the points stressed by Anne (the next patient to be described)—that not until she was in hospital had she begun to appreciate the value of a routine job, routine getting up in the morning; the change from a bohemian outlook to a more conformist one—from a freedom-loving, rebellious, beatnik-like behaviour to a more 'square' attitude, seems to have been an important factor in the stories of the three 'recovered' patients described in this book.

CASE II

Anne is now 25 years old, single, living with a friend, working steadily, and has not taken any drugs since leaving hospital two-and-a-half years ago, having previously taken cannabis, amphetamines and heroin. An edited transcript of an interview with her follows:

Question: Could you please tell us something about your home background? And do you think this may have any bearing on your having started on drugs?

Anne: Well, I was not happy at home. My mother had died when I was 4 years old. My father was a heavy drinker and very strict. I did not get on with him, and he behaved badly to me, so when I was 16 I began to go to the West End and shortly afterwards I began to take pills and to 'fix'.

Question: What were your reasons for going to the West End and your starting on drugs?

Anne: Initially to feel 'big'.

Question: Could you tell us a bit more about your childhood please?

Anne: I was born during the War. I think my parents were quite happy together. Then my mother died of T.B. I never really knew her, so I did not miss her. After her death, I and my younger sister were sent away to foster parents. We were quite happy there and went to primary school. My father took us back home when I was 8 or 9, and I went to a secondary modern school till I was 15. I failed the 11-plus, but I was quite happy at school.

Question: What did you do after leaving school?

Anne: I started work as a trainee hairdresser in south east London. I liked the work, but I left after six months because I did not get enough money. Then I earned good money working in a factory for a while from the age of 16 or so.

Question: Could you tell us more about the start of your drug taking?

Anne: Well, I did not get on with my father when I was 15 or 16 because of his heavy drinking. He changed very much when drinking, becoming very strict and sometimes violent. That was when I began to go to the West End and stay out all night. I liked the music, and in order to stay awake at night-time I started taking pills—Preludin. The trouble was that taking the pills I could not sleep at night at home and I was up half the night; so my father found out about my drug taking and I got a good hiding, and I ran away from home when I was 16 or 17.

Question : How did you get the pills ?

Anne : I took Preludin, Dexedrine, and Drinamyl, all of which I bought on the black market. I never had any on a doctor's prescription, I would not know what to say to a doctor to get the stuff. I started with several tablets a day, and built them up till after four months or so, I was taking up to 35 or 40 pills a day ... I also took Nostroline (*a proprietary nasal inhalant*), chewing its cotton wool. Because of all these pills I could not sleep, and therefore, at the same time, I also took marijuana to help me to go to sleep.

Question : When did you start heroin ?

Anne : I stayed on pills for about one-and-a-half years, then started fixing heroin after being introduced to it at a party. I began to take it regularly, mainly 'skin-popping'. Sometimes I did 'mainlining', but the effect was too sudden and I preferred skin-popping. I fixed about 2/3 of a grain of heroin three or four times a day. Occasionally I also had cocaine but this gave me nausea and I never took cocaine regularly.

Question : How did you get hold of heroin ?

Anne : I got it from 'registered' addicts, paying about £1 for 2/3 of a grain. I earned the money by various means. I have been on heroin regularly, except for a spell in Borstal, for one-and-a-half years, for forgery and false pretences. As I was not working I had to get money in order to pay for the drugs. (*At the time of coming to hospital she was on Borstal licence and the probation officer did not know that she was again taking drugs.*) I never managed then to stay off heroin longer than a few weeks. It makes me relaxed. (*However, she kept off heroin for a week or so before entering hospital as the friend she was living with strongly encouraged her to give up heroin. Instead, she had been again on Preludin and Drinamyl—about* 40 *per day : 'Pills just make me talk a lot and make my mind go blank'. At the time she was admitted to hospital in* 1964 (*aged* 23) *she stated that she wanted to come off drugs and lead a normal life, as she was getting depressed and sitting indoors all the time. Her sister who had never been on drugs was getting married.* 'I would have never dreamt of introducing my younger sister to the West End and to drugs!' *However, other young addicts who were present at a later group meeting when Anne made this statement claimed to have known cases where addicted youths introduced their younger brothers to the drug habit*).

Question : How did you get into trouble with the Law ?

Anne : When I had no money left to buy drugs, and I could not work because of my taking drugs, I started to forge cheques. I also obtained clothes by false pretences and sold them, and with the money I bought drugs. When caught I was put on probation for two years on condition I was living at home. I broke probation because I felt I could not settle down at home, and because I liked the excitement of the West End. I was arrested soon afterwards and committed to Borstal training for two years. However, the day after leaving Borstal I was back on heroin; after a few days I took an overdose by mistake and was taken to hospital. Again, the day after leaving that hospital I started on heroin again, but then I got fed up with drug taking; I met my new friend and I decided to try to come off heroin. I managed with the help of pills, but I went through agonies. I went to my G.P. who referred me to hospital.

(*Anne stayed in hospital for three months. After a stormy beginning, when she was very temperamental—on one occasion smashing a window—she settled down, participating actively in the group meetings. Since leaving she stayed off drugs, but a year-and-a-half after discharge she asked for a temporary readmission as a precautionary measure as she had become anxious, tense, and depressed; she stayed in hospital for a fortnight and has been feeling well ever since.*)

Question: How have you got on since leaving hospital?

Anne: Well, in hospital, although I did not like it at first I learned to live in a routine way, to get up regularly in the morning, to do a routine job steadily, all things I had never done before. I have carried on like this since leaving hospital. I am now working as a shop assistant. Initially for a few months after leaving hospital I worked as a cinema usherette in a West End cinema, but I met there too many addicts who ridiculed me for working, and this upset me a great deal. So I left and took on my present job. I now live outside the West End. I am working hard, feeling tired in the evening and sleeping well. I avoid addicts and I am keeping away from the clubs where people used to take drugs. I am still lacking confidence in mixing with people.

Question: How about drugs?

Anne: I never had any since leaving hospital, and I had no alcohol, which I do not like anyway—but I take more ordinary cigarettes than formerly. (*Anne had started to smoke cigarettes whilst on remand in prison and whilst being withdrawn from heroin.*) My worst period was six months after leaving hospital; as I felt guilty about my past, I wanted to stay in the dark and therefore chose an usherette job in a cinema and I met many addicts . . . I had a strong mental craving for drugs even after my 'physical' addiction had cleared up, which lasted for five months . . . I never meant to play up in hospital, but everything was so much on top of me in the first few days that I smashed . . . I had a gnawing feeling in my tummy for five months. Even now, more than two years after leaving hospital, I still feel sometimes sick in the morning when I am tense or upset, and I feel sick whenever I see syringes or 'addicts' in TV plays. But I get sad when I see others back on stuff again; a lot of addicts are taking liquid Methedrine with 'sleepers' now—it is getting worse, and they seem to be so young; they all seem to be trying to get 'registered' as if it was the thing to do.

Question: What are the factors that you think helped you to keep off drugs?

Anne: I have an understanding friend who encourages me, and with whom I am able to discuss my problems. In hospital I learned to appreciate routine and I am working regularly, also doing overtime to get extra money. I keep away from other addicts as much as I can, and maintain many contacts with people not using drugs. I keep in touch with the hospital and the meetings. I got a lot of help in hospital from Ed (*the recovered Canadian addict described earlier*) who encouraged me and explained matters to me.

REFERENCE

1. *Drug Addiction* (1961) Report of the Interdepartmental Committee. H.M.S.O., London.

8 Mortality Rates of British Addicts*

Unfortunately, at present, chances for the heroin and cocaine addict to recover are relatively poor, and highlight the urgent need for a programme of prevention (including here the training of the medical and other professions involved; the education of the general public, with special emphasis on the young; and a programme of planned research), early institution of treatment, and the provision of a sufficient number of well-equipped and well-staffed treatment and after-care facilities (including half-way houses, vocational training, etc.). How important and urgent this task is can be seen from a review of the fate that may befall the person dependent on hard drugs. It is true that an American investigator (Winick)[1] has found that some narcotic addicts may 'mature out' of their addiction, i.e. that they may give up drug taking after the age of 40 or so but there has been no evidence put forward so far that this is likely to occur among the young, non-therapeutic British heroin and cocaine addict. How is he likely to fare if there are not soon important improvements made in the arrangements and facilities to bring him help?

An excellent survey of suicide and mortality amongst non-therapeutic addicts in Britain has recently been made by Dr. I. P. James,[2] based on Home Office records. The survey covers the decade 1955–1965, during which period 450 new heroin addicts became known to the Home Office; at the end of this period 342 (i.e. 3 in 4) were still receiving heroin on prescription. This, incidentally, is of some interest in view of the claim often made by those doctors who were in the habit of prescribing these drugs to addicts that the aim was to establish a positive relationship with the addict in order to motivate him as soon as possible to accept hospital treatment for complete withdrawal; clearly in the great majority of cases—whatever the original

* The first part of this chapter is based on I. P. James (1967) Suicide and Mortality amongst Heroin Addicts in Britain, *Brit. J. Addict.*, **62**.

intentions—this had not happened, whether due to the failure of the practitioners in motivating the addict towards giving up drugs, or to the failure of the hospital treatment. The above statistics highlight again the great dangers of introducing youngsters, without careful check-up to the routine of regular prescribing as more often than not it seems that, once introduced, they are not very likely to give up drugs. This ratio, 3 in 4, also highlights the great importance—when implementing the new 1967 Law—of urging and motivating the addicts who have opted for maintenance prescribing towards an early alteration of their views; otherwise they may be expected to go on using drugs, with the risk of an early death as described later.

Of the 450 new addicts, almost all (436—321 men and 115 women) were non-therapeutic in origin. The great majority—334, i.e. 3 in 4—were British-born (among these, one-third (110) were women); of the remainder, the majority were Canadians (70, of whom 9 were female), and 32 (6 female) were of other nationalities. As referred to in the discussion of the recovered Canadian addict, the Canadians were addicted before their arrival in this country in the early 1960's, attracted by their knowledge that they would be able to live here in peace and freedom, without fear of the law, whilst continuing to take drugs. Again, as referred to in an earlier discussion, it is not surprising to find that the average Canadian addict—who by that time had been a practising addict for several years—was, at the time he was first recorded after his arrival in this country, an older person than his British counterpart, the respective approximate mean ages being 32 and 24 years respectively. In the few years since Dr. James's survey the average age of the British heroin addict has decreased, and nowadays one comes across quite a few youngsters who start fixing at as early an age as 15 or 16. Despite—or because of—the greater interest in the problem starting at that time, more and more new young heroin addicts were added to the ranks; thus in 1964 alone, 161 became 'known' who first had begun to use heroin illicitly before being taken on by doctors, and since then this number has increased steadily: 259 new non-therapeutic heroin addicts in 1965; 522 in 1966. Most countries have discontinued the medical use of heroin following a recommendation by the International Narcotic Commission. In Britain the Government (in 1956) reversed its decision to adopt a similar course, following strong protests from some medical circles that for certain medical and surgical conditions heroin was irreplaceable. As far as cocaine is concerned, nowadays there seems little justification for its medical use; but of the non-therapeutic addicts, 2 in 3 combined their use of heroin with that of cocaine, and most were receiving both drugs regularly on prescription from doctors. The use of cocaine by addicts is much less common in North America than in this country, and one may question the advisability of regular prescribing of cocaine, whatever its justification in the case of heroin. Certainly addicts themselves (who often proclaim the slogan: heroin for Health, cocaine for Kicks) as a rule declare that cocaine is the more dangerous drug. The effect of cocaine is so transient that addicts have to keep on fixing very frequently throughout the day in order to stay in the drug-induced conditions, thus leaving little time, energy or interest in any activities not connected with their drug taking.

What is the *mortality* of these non-therapeutic heroin addicts? In the decade 1955–1965, out of 321 men (often not much more than boys) 35 had died; out of 115 women, 4. The male mortality rate—11 in 100—over a mean period at risk of just over four years, amounts to 27 deaths per 1,000 per year. This death rate among male heroin addicts is—according to Dr. James's calculations—twenty times as high as the total mortality rate which could be expected for a male population of similar age composition. The female deaths are so few that they do not lend themselves to significant statistical calculations; the death rate of just over 3% is considerably lower than that of the men, and, for what it is worth, is more than five times the expected mortality rate.

How did these people die? Of the 35 males at least 5, and very likely 4 more, died wilfully from their own hands (i.e. if one were to assume that the minds of these men, after years of maltreating their minds and bodies with these dangerous drugs and after years of starvation and neglect, etc., were still capable of proper functioning and of rational reasoning and weighing up the pros and cons of their actions).

Of the 5 definite suicides, 2 died by using a violent method (hanging), 2 from poisoning, and 1 from coal gas asphyxia. The 'probable' suicides are individuals on whom the official inquest recorded an 'open verdict', but the circumstances strongly indicated a suicide; they all had taken a large overdose of a drug to which they were not actively addicted, and 3 of them had made previous suicidal attempts. Compared to a normal population corrected for age, the suicide rates among these male addicts was over fifty times as high.

Apart from the 4 who died from a probably intentional overdosage with a drug they had not been accustomed to, there were 12 others who died from an apparently unintentional overdose of the drug to which they were addicted, i.e. as a rule heroin, alone or in combination with cocaine; in 4 cases methadone, morphine, or barbiturate (alone or with heroin) were responsible. (All these drugs were sometimes prescribed by practitioners to heroin addicts, barbiturates at times in very high doses.) Occasional death was associated with the phenomenon of a waning of the acquired tolerance to heroin after a period of abstinence in prison or in hospital, a danger to which reference has already been made. Cases are known in which similar events took place with a non-fatal outcome; but 2 with a fatal outcome refer first to one individual who died in this way shortly after he had been released from prison, and to another who obtained heroin on prescription whilst on a day pass from hospital, where he had been undergoing treatment for two months, and who was found dead next day in the hospital lavatory.

Fourteen further deaths among the 321 were due to other causes, in 4 cases as a consequence of septic conditions; the habit of these people of neglecting the most elementary precautions regarding sterile needles, cleaning up the injection areas, etc., is fraught with great danger, and their arms are often covered with scars. Many fortunately survive, but conditions such as septicaemia and bacterial endocarditis were involved in this group of deaths.

Apparently, no-one during the period in question died as a consequence of a hepatitis following an infection transmitted through the use of non-sterilized syringes, although jaundice from this cause is not very uncommon in addicts who are in the habit of using common syringes and needles. Three addicts died suddenly, 1 from the inhalation of vomit during a drug-withdrawal fit (addicts themselves are keen on stressing the dangers of withdrawal, and the risk of inhalation of vomit is well known to them). Three addicts died a violent death, 2 through falling from heights, and 1 in a motor accident. Again, addicts know these dangers, one for example recently describing graphically how in a 'stoned' state he had stepped out in front of a car, been knocked·down and suffered multiple injuries.

How old were these addicts at the time of their death? Their mean age at the time was 31·5 years, that of the 23 British-born addicts of 30·3 years being slightly less than that of the 12 non-British group of 33·5 years. The average age of those who died wilfully—usually through taking overdoses of drugs with suicidal intent—was 29·1 years; that is, two-and-a-half years later than those dying from accidentally giving themselves too-high doses of their narcotic drugs (average age at death: 26·9 years). Those who died from accidental drug overdose or by suicide shortened their life span by several years, the mean age at death of the 14 addicts who died from causes other than suicide or accidental overdose being 36·5 years. Even this, of course, means a shortening of life by over thirty years.

All in all, Dr. James's survey presents a very sombre picture. Youngsters who take up the heroin and cocaine habit—for reasons often no more than being curious, bored or discontented—and who go on to find a practitioner (or, in the future, the officially recognized 'prescribing or maintenance centres'—unless their method of handling addicts becomes vastly superior to the one evolved by present-day 'junkie doctors') run a risk of dying within the next few years; that is, per year, twenty times as high than in the case of the person who does not become dependent on drugs. The life span of addicts is shortened by many years even if they escape the risk of taking fatal overdoses of their drug of addiction, and even if they are able to avoid the feeling of hopelessness and despair which drives quite a few addicts into suicide fifty times as often as non-addicted individuals of the same age groups.

As we have seen, over the past few years youngsters have joined the ranks of the heroin and cocaine addicts at an increasing pace. The number of new heroin addicts who became known to the Home Office during the years from 1955 to 1960 was 72, during the years 1961 to 1964, 378. During 1965 and 1966 the pace accelerated even further (259 and 522 new heroin addicts respectively were added to the Index during this period) and an ever-increasing proportion of the new heroin addicts were youngsters, non-therapeutic in origin. What was the effect of these additional addicted youngsters in the recent years on the mortality rate and the ages of death? A rough, provisional review of deaths of heroin addicts in the period from April 1965 (when Dr James's study had ended) until March 1967 shows 28 male and 6 female deaths, all of them apparently non-therapeutic addicts as far as can be ascertained. Thus there were only 5 fewer deaths (34) during the most recent two-year period than during the preceding total decade (39). Compared to the 1955–1965 decade, the ratio between the mortality of the British-born to the non-British-born addicts had greatly increased over the recent two-year period; of the 28 male deaths in 1965–1967, 23 were British-born, only 5 non-British, as against the former ratio of 23 to 12. The mean age at death of the 28 males in the recent period (29·4 years) was two years less than during the preceding decade (31·5 years). The shift in ages at the time of death becomes much more obvious when looking separately at the mean ages of death of the 23 British-born (i.e. 27·3 years), and the 5 non-British-born (i.e. 39·0 years); the marked age difference of nearly 12 years between the British and non-British group contrasts strongly with an age difference of only 3 years in Dr. James's earlier sample, when the mean age at death of the British was 30·3 years and that of the non-British, 33·5 years. The difference is obvious from a quick glance at Table 3.

Table 3. Mortality of male heroin addicts

	1955–March 1965 (10 years)			April 1965–March 1967 (2 years)	
	Number	Mean age (years)	Median age	Number	Mean age (years)
British-born	23	30·3	24·0	23	27·3
Non-British-born	12	33·5	37·0	5	39·0
All addicts	35	31·5	25·0	28	29·4

There is a large difference of almost $4\frac{1}{2}$ years between the median and the mean ages (25 and 29·4 years, respectively) of death of the addicts who died in the recent two-year period. (The mean is the average, whereas the median is the middle value when all values are considered in order of ages; the median age for the British group alone, whose ages at death varied from 17 to 44, amounting to 24·0 years; for the whole of the recent group, with a range of ages of death between 17 and

98

48, 25·0 years.) This large difference between the median and the mean ages of death indicates a bimodal distribution, i.e. the presence of two peaks of maximum frequency of death ages with relatively few cases in between, in contrast to the ideal normal distribution where the intermediate age groups would have been mainly affected, and the very young and the relatively old (relatively old, that is, as regards the ages of heroin addicts) only rarely. This bimodal distribution thus reflects the division of heroin addicts at age of death into two fairly clear-cut sections; a younger one and an older. A glance at Table 3 shows that this division is likely to correspond largely to that between the British and the non-British groups or between the 'new wave' of the young addicts and the older wave. Of the 23 British addicts who died in 1965–1967, 15 were 25 years old and younger, 5 were between 26 and 30, and only 3 were above 30 years; the ages of the non-British were 30, 36, 44, and 48. It is thus clear that not only do the youngsters in this country become addicted to heroin in increasing numbers, but also that of those who have become addicted, a high proportion are likely to die at a relatively young age.

Thus more and more youngsters take up the heroin habit, more become addicted and become 'registered', most of those 'registered' go on obtaining the drug on prescription rather than dropping off after a short period, and of those addicted a high proportion are likely to die at a relatively early age. It is difficult to see how in such circumstances any talk of 'panic measures' can be maintained; surely it is high time for something to be done. Nobody knows what consequences any radical changes in the British system may bring with them; but that something has to be done to stem the tide seems obvious from the above mortality considerations.

REFERENCES

1. Winick, C. (1962) Maturing Out of Narcotic Addiction. *Bull. Narcot.,* **14,** 1.
2. James, I. Pierce (1967) Suicide and Mortality amongst Heroin Addicts in Britain. *Brit. J. Addict.,* **62.**

9 The Legal Aspects of the Heroin-Cocaine Problem in Britain: Past Present ... and the Future?*

In order to understand fully the recommendations made by the Second Report of the Interdepartmental Committee in 1965,[1] it is necessary to review briefly the suggestions made by earlier committees as regards drug addiction. This is also important because a great deal of interest has been taken abroad in the working of the so-called 'British system'; the interest shown has not prevented a lot of misunderstanding.

Controls on narcotic drugs in Great Britain were first imposed by the Dangerous Drugs Act of 1920, which aimed at the control of the non-legitimate trade in the specified dangerous drugs (such as the opiates and cocaine) without interfering with their legitimate medical administration. However, ambiguities remained as to whether the treatment of addicts could be regarded as legitimate medical practice. As a result, a few years later the Departmental Committee on Morphine and Heroin Addiction was appointed which published in 1926 the so-called Rolleston Report. In it a distinction was drawn between providing drugs to addicts under suitable controls and supplying them merely for the 'gratification of addiction'. Indications were outlined as to when morphine or heroin could be given 'properly': i.e. to 'patients ... under treatment by the gradual withdrawal method with a view to cure', or where it had been' demonstrated, after prolonged attempt at cure, that the ... drug cannot be safely discontinued entirely' because of severe withdrawal symptoms, or where 'it has been similarly demonstrated that the patient, while capable of leading a useful and relatively normal life when a certain minimum dose is

* Based, in part, on M. M. Glatt (1966) A Review of the Second Report of the Interdepartmental Committee on Drug Addiction, *Bull. Narcot.*, **18**, 31–45.

regularly administered, becomes incapable of this when the drug is entirely discontinued'. Certain 'precautions' were outlined in the report which practitioners were requested to observe when treating addicts by a method of gradual withdrawal and when administering the drugs to apparently incurable patients. When treating addicts by gradual withdrawal, the practitioner should keep in mind that 'the primary object of the treatment is the cure of the addiction, if practicable'. Therefore if possible the patient should be induced to enter an institution; when he is unable or refuses to do so the doctor 'must attempt to cure his condition by steady, judicious reduction of the dose'. Whenever in any doubt or difficulties, the doctor 'must consider whether he can properly continue indefinitely to bear the sole responsibility for the treatment ... (and) ... accept the responsibility of supplying or ordering indefinitely the drug of addiction in the minimum doses which seem necessary'. In cases like these the report suggested that doctors would be 'well advised to obtain a second opinion on the case'. In the second group, the apparently incurable cases, the doctor was reminded that his 'main object must be to keep the supply of the drug within the limits of what is strictly necessary'. When faced with a new patient the doctor 'should not supply or order the drug unless satisfied as to the urgency' and should not accede to the addict's request for further administration without 'obtaining' from the previous medical attendant an account of the nature of the case'.

The Rolleston Report's proposals led at that time to certain amendments to the Dangerous Drugs Regulations. They included the provision of a tribunal in cases where doctors were thought to supply, administer or prescribe drugs 'for purposes other than medical treatment'; medical treatment was the only indication allowed for prescribing such drugs. However, these tribunals never materialized and were at any rate rejected by the 1961 Report of the Interdepartmental Committee.

THE (FIRST) REPORT OF THE INTERDEPARTMENTAL COMMITTEE, 1961

The Rolleston Report of 1926 dealt mainly with morphine and heroin addiction. Soon new analgesics were put on the market

—other opiates or synthetic preparations which were, sooner or later, also found to be dependence-producing drugs, whatever hopes to the contrary might have existed initially. Treatment of the withdrawal symptoms had been a major concern of the Rolleston Report; in the subsequent years newer, improved methods began to supersede the older, cruder techniques. Thus it was found possible to replace the older addictive drugs by newer dependence-producing drugs—such as methadone (Physeptone)—which then could be withdrawn more easily than the older addictive drugs; also many symptoms of the withdrawal period could be relieved by using members of a newly introduced group of substances widely employed in other branches of psychiatry—the tranquillizers—which, with rare exceptions, have so far not shown themselves to be addictive. Developments such as these prompted the Government in 1958 to appoint an Interdepartmental Committee on Drug Addiction which was 'to review ... the advice given by the Rolleston Committee in 1926 including the possible application of any new suggestions to other addictive or habit-forming drugs; and to advise on any possible need for additional special treatment facilities or administrative measures'. However, the report published in 1961 found that there was little to worry about as regards the drug situation, and no need for radical changes. The incidence of addiction to dangerous drugs was found to be still small despite the slight post-war increase shown by Home Office figures of the numbers of addicts to certain drugs, such as morphine, heroin, cocaine, pethidine, methadone, and phenadoxone. In the Committee's view this increase merely reflected the greater vigilance in detecting and recognizing the addicts. Nor was the Committee perturbed about illicit traffic, which was regarded as 'so small as to be almost negligible'. In the Committee's view two sets of factors contributed towards the maintenance of this relatively satisfactory state of affairs. First, the social attitudes of the British public to law observance in general, and to the taking of dangerous drugs in particular; and second, the systematic enforcement of the Regulations of the Dangerous Drugs Act, 1951. The Committee was at pains to dispel the misconception—widely held not only abroad, but also at home, and even among addicts themselves—that a system of 'registration' existed in Great Britain (and it rejected the notion that 'registration' was desirable or helpful) which

'entitled (such addicts) to receive dangerous drugs on prescription'. What in fact was true was that 'the continued provision of supplies to patient addicts depends solely on the
individual decision made by the medical practitioner pro-
fessionally responsible for each case'. The Committee felt
satisfied that the right of British doctors 'to continue at their
own professional discretion the provision of dangerous drugs
to known addicts has not contributed to any increase in the
total number of patients receiving regular supplies in this
way' (a view which the second Report only four years later was
forced to revise), and that despite the absence of a system of
registration nearly all addicts were known to the authorities
(another supposition which certainly was no longer true only
a few years later), because of the arrangements made for
recording manufacture and supply, and for inspection. The
Report, however, enjoined doctors not to issue prescriptions
to addicts 'without providing adequate medical supervision
without making any determined efforts at withdrawal, and,
notably, without seeking another medical opinion'; and the
second opinion should be obtained in writing before doctors
embarked on the regular prescribing of a dangerous drug for
a lengthy period, 'say, in excess of three months'. Moreover,
a practitioner should prescribe only a limited amount of a
dangerous drug to a patient temporarily under his care in the
absence of a letter from the patient's own doctor.

On the whole the state of affairs was regarded as satisfactory
by the Committee in 1961. The Report stated specifically that
at the time no doctor was known to follow practices other than
the recommended ones. Yet no more than four years later the
Government felt it necessary to reconvene the Committee in
order to decide whether, in the light of experience in the mean-
time, the role of doctors in relation to the prescribing of addictive drugs needed revising. What had gone wrong?

Going back in our story once again more than forty years,
the Rolleston Committee had been convened because of
occasional reports that a doctor had ordered morphine and
heroin 'simply to satisfy the craving of the addict', or had
'prescribed the drugs in large quantities ... to persons previously unknown to the practitioner or to a patient receiving
supplies elsewhere'. Such practices were again 'strongly condemned' by the (first) report of the Interdepartmental Committee in 1961 which criticized the issue of prescriptions to

addicts 'without making any determined effort at withdrawal, and, notably, without seeking another medical opinion'. The 1961 report noted with satisfaction that only two habitual offenders during the preceding twenty years had come to its notice. But in the years that elapsed between the 1961 and the 1965 Interdepartmental Committee's Reports there occurred a shift of opinion in certain medical circles as to what constituted good medical practice in the management of drug-dependent patients. For example, psychiatrists working with addicts in hospitals were told again and again that they had found no difficulty whatsoever in obtaining supplies of heroin and cocaine from certain medical practitioners without these doctors having made 'any ... effort at withdrawal', and in receiving such supplies regularly, frequently in increasing dosage, without the doctors' ever calling in 'another medical opinion'—practices which, after all, had been 'strongly condemned' by the 1961 Interdepartmental Committee. Again and again addicts stated that a regime of regular prescribing had been started by private or National Health Service general practitioners without a preceding 'prolonged attempt at cure', without calling in a second opinion, without ascertaining whether the applicant did lead 'a useful, fairly normal life whilst taking a non-progressive amount of drugs' (most young addicts soon stopped working after going on regular heroin and cocaine prescriptions, living on National Assistance, not infrequently augmenting their 'income' by pushing, etc.), or alternatively, whether the addict ceased to be able to lead a useful, gainful life when the drug was withdrawn. Instead of first attempting to motivate the addict towards undergoing treatment to come off drugs before initiating a regime of regular prescribing, these (few) doctors felt that the right method was to start regular prescribing in the first instance in the hope of establishing a good doctor-patient relationship under which the doctor might find it easier to persuade the addict to come off drugs. As it turned out, the figures quoted, in Chapter 8 showing that by the end of 1964 as many as 3 in 4. of the 'registered' addicts continued to receive regular prescriptions, illustrate that such hopes were often not realized. In the view of the Second Report published in 1965 it was the activities of a handful of doctors who prescribed excessive amounts to individual patients that constituted the main source of the supplies of the dangerous drugs which led to an

increase in the number of addicts. Nevertheless, the Report
stressed that these doctors had 'acted within the Law and
according to their professional judgment'. Clearly, it was
possible for practitioners to ignore some of the recommendations of the 1926 and the 1961 Committees and still to be
acting 'within the Law'. The explanation might lie in certain
other statements of the 1961 Committee, which mentioned the
possibility that 'a doctor who appears to be prescribing
excessively for a particular patient may claim that he is doing
so for adequate medical reasons', and adding that 'without
interfering with his professional freedom it would be difficult
to contest such an assertion'. Moreover, in the Committee's
view the number of addicts in the country was too small to
warrant the opening of specialized treatment establishments,
although in its view addicts could be treated satisfactorily only
in suitable institutions; yet it regarded the compulsory com-
mittal of addicts to institutions as 'not desirable'. Thus the
position was that a practitioner faced with a patient claiming
to be an addict and requesting a supply of drugs could not
compel him to enter hospital for an assessment as to whether
he really needed drugs and, if he did, in what quantity; at the
same time it is impossible under conditions of general practice
(and difficult even in hospital) to come to even an approximate
estimate of the patient's genuine needs. The practitioner might,
well feel, therefore, that in prescribing in such circumstances
he was doing so 'for adequate medical reasons'.

No less confusing than the exact state of the Law as regards
prescribing of addictive drugs in this country, was the view
held abroad on the British system, especially in the U.S.A.
There many medical authorities felt that when contrasted
with the restrictive, punitive approach to the addict 'criminal'
the permissive British practices offered a great many funda-
mental advantages. For example, unlike the American addict,
driven underground and into the arms of the black market
through not being able to acquire the drugs he needed legitimately, his British counterpart could quite openly and legally
obtain his drugs from the G.P. and thus there was no need for
a black market. (In practice, as we have seen in the preceding
chapters, things unfortunately did not quite work out this way.)
The British system seemed even more attractive when reports
appeared of successful therapeutic methods based on it. Thus,
an article published by two London doctors in 1960 described a

technique consisting of treating addicts in two phases: in the first, addicts were supplied with drugs whilst being 'stabilized'; where it seemed indicated, extra supplies were prescribed to forestall a return of these patients to the black market. After some time, this procedure was followed by the second phase in which an attempt was made to withdraw the addict from his drugs. The good results reported with this method were bound to attract attention, especially in North America, and—as described previously—in subsequent years quite a few addicts arrived in Britain (mainly from Canada), attracted by the liberal, permissive approach. In the beginning, mainly private practitioners prescribed addictive drugs regularly to addicts; later on, certain National Health Service doctors, feeling that it was unfair that addicts without private means were not able to obtain the drugs they needed, opened their practices to addicts. The article written by the two London doctors (cited above) claimed that the black market in Britain had died away as a result of their prescribing practice. As we have seen, these hopes and claims were not borne out by the subsequent course of events; 'registered' addicts sold their surplus of drugs, thus introducing more and more newcomers to the drug habit.

THE SECOND REPORT OF THE INTERDEPARTMENTAL COMMITTEE, 1965

The 'new situation' which the second Brain Committee* faced (in view of the alarming increase of non-therapeutic young addicts) required certain new measures. Whatever other factors might have been at work, the main reason for the addiction epidemic, in the Committee's views, was the prescribing habits of a few doctors. Among the steps suggested in 1965, therefore was that although addicts would still be treated as sick people and not as criminals, such treatment would no longer be carried out by G.P.s but in special treatment centres—especially in the London area (where the need is greatest), but also in selected hospitals in other regions. Facilities for laboratory investigations and for research were to be made available at such centres. Only doctors on the staff of such centres would have the right to prescribe

* Lord Brain, who died in 1966, was Chairman of both the 1958 and the reconvened Interdepartmental Committees.

heroin and cocaine to addicts. Should other practitioners prescribe such drugs to an addict (curiously enough, other addictive drugs were not so restricted, despite the obvious dangers that addicts might switch to a new, possibly equally addictive and harmful substitute), it would constitute a statutory offence. Treatment centres were also to be given the right —by means of new legislation—to detain addicts compulsorily during a withdrawal crisis. Compulsory notification of addicts to a central authority was to be introduced—'notification' rather than 'registration' to avoid fostering the misconception of an addict's right to his supply of drugs. Finally, a Standing Advisory Committee was to be set up, in order to keep the continually shifting drug scene under constant review, including the possible misuse of any drug acting on the central nervous system and likely to cause dependence.

The Second Report's reversal in several important aspects of recommendations made four years earlier naturally evoked different reactions and comments. The most obvious criticism levelled at the Report by the censured 'prescribing doctors' was that the addict in need of drugs would get them by hook or by crook; if not legitimately from their G.P.s, then from the black market. However, most unbiassed observers would probably agree that the fear of a large-scale imported black market could not provide an excuse for maintaining one produced and continued by doctors' overprescribing. Another criticism of the Report was that, by not coming to grips with the core of the problem, it had made the 'prescribing doctors' a scapegoat. On the other hand, whilst nobody would doubt the great importance of wider social issues involved, such as the presence in the community of a much greater number than ever before of teenagers—many of them affluent, bored, searching for 'kicks', thrills, new experiences—should not the knowledge of the presence of this vast, potentially vulnerable reservoir make it even more imperative to be cautious in one's prescribing habits of highly dangerous drugs? There is obviously a clear need for fact-finding research in this field—but had the Brain Committee (as has been argued by some critics) tried to study closely all the manifold aspects involved, it would have taken years before any recommendations could have been made. Meanwhile the overprescribing would have gone on, and with it the resulting contribution to the increase of addiction among youngsters. The suggestion of excluding G.P.s from treating addicts naturally came in for much criticism; one might hope that interested G.P.s would be given a change to colla-borate with (or within) the proposed centres. Then there was criticism raised as to why action was taken, in a way, against all G.P.s rather than against the small number who had come under fire (because the great majority of G.P.s have kept aloof so far from the treatment of addicts). As it turned out, whilst some of the overprescribing doctors changed their practice to some extent, others soon took their place. One important question arising from the Report concerns the lack of suitable medical and other staff to man these centres and to carry out the all-important after-care programme; one would feel that interested and suitably trained G.P.s could make an important contribution here.

The conclusions arrived at by the second Brain Report confirmed that there no longer existed the clear-cut differences between the British and American drug scenes which, for example, Schur had described only four years earlier when con-trasting the British system with the American approach (cf. Chapter 2). No longer was it true that a high proportion of British addicts were professional and middle aged and that there were few young addicts in this country. No longer was it true that there was no drug addict subculture and little use of 'a special addict argot' or slang; no longer true either that there was no peddling of drugs between addicts (although there was no evidence of an imported black market). The permissive British system had not been able to prevent the gradual emergence of an addictive drugs problem as its many protagonists across the Atlantic had claimed it did. The hope that, just by allowing doctors to prescribe such drugs freely to addicts without any real attempt at some form of restriction, one would solve or even avoid the emergence of a drug problem had proved wrong. The hard, close look which the members of the Interdepart-mental Committee had been compelled to take at their second try had shown that certain alterations had to be made, whilst still avoiding a punitive approach and emphasizing the addict's need for medico-social treatment.

THE DANGEROUS DRUGS BILL, 1967

The Second Report of the Interdepartmental Committee pub-lished in the Autumn of 1965 had indicated to the authorities, the medical profession, and the general public, the urgent necessity to come to grips with the whole complex question of drug dependence and the need for constant vigilance in this field. What was to be done about it? And when? For more than a year, in fact, nothing seemed to happen—possibly because of the difficulties in implementing some of the Committee's suggestions. Probably the great majority of observers felt that the present system of free prescribing by doctors could not be allowed to go on, but the fear lurking in everybody's mind was the possible emergence of a large-scale imported black market on American lines, for the sizeable number of addicts provided a profitable market. There were also voices heard against taking 'panic measures'; but one might question whether there would have been the urgent need for drastic steps today, had warning voices in the early 1960's been heeded then, and had there been less complacency. The Standing Advisory Committee suggested by the Brain Committee was formed late in 1966. However, the numbers of young heroin and cocaine addicts 'known' to the Home Office kept increasing at a quickened pace (279 new cases of heroin addiction in the first nine months of 1966) and, by now, everybody was agreed that— unlike the views expressed in the 1961 Report—a high proportion of addicts was not (perhaps 'not yet') known to the Home Office. Many were obtaining their drugs on what was described earlier in this volume as the 'pseudo black market' by buying from 'registered' addicts for a number of months before going to doctors and becoming 'known'. A report published in *The Times* quoted the Vera Institute of New York as forecasting 11,000 heroin addicts in Great Britain by 1972. Meanwhile, as we have seen, some of the criticized doctors seemed to have altered their prescribing habits, but others were taking their place. Excessive prescribing was still reported by addicts to be going on, and still is at the time this book is being finished (June 1967). Certain other practices criticized in the past continued too, such as the habit by certain doctors of prescribing to very young addicts without informing their usual National Health Service practitioner or their parents who, by then, having found out about their child's drug taking had often been trying hard to get and to keep him off drugs. As more and more reports of drugs being found in possession of very young people began to appear in the newspapers, public concern became widespread. Whilst there obviously exists an urgent need for objective, sound information and education in this field among the general public and in particular amongst youngsters, one might question whether the way in which the information was presented in the papers was always of a helpful nature; addicts themselves were often critical, pointing out for example that reports of famous pop stars taking drugs might have the effect of encouraging their highly suggestible, young fans to follow in their footsteps. The problem of how to make and to keep youngsters aware of the risks involved in starting on drugs without glamorizing them, and without inducing curiosity is one bound to present many difficulties in the future.

The medical profession also began to take a greater interest in the problem as demonstrated, for example, in the attendance of several hundreds of doctors at an international symposium on drug taking organized by the Society for the Study of Addiction in London in September 1966. Steps to be taken on the drug problem were outlined in the House of Commons on 30th January 1967. On 8th March 1967 the Ministry of Health issued a Memorandum on 'The Treatment and Supervision of Heroin Addiction' for the guidance of hospital authorities. A fortnight later the Home Secretary introduced a Dangerous Drugs Bill. The Memorandum points to the advantages of treating those addicts who agree to come off drugs, in small groups, preferably of no more than twelve in a group. For those addicts who do not consent to the giving up of drugs, outpatient services are envisaged. A table giving the distribution of heroin addicts known to the Home Office in January 1967 shows that of the total of 659 (a figure likely to be very much of an underestimate), 467, i.e. nearly 3 in 4, live in the London Postal District. If one includes the 100 'known' addicts living within the catchment areas of the Metropolitan Regional Hospital Boards (outside the London Postal District), the proportion among known addicts who will have to be catered for in, and close to, London rises to over 85%. (The only other sizeable populations of 'known' addicts are in Birmingham (47)—possibly because a special clinic has been looking after and prescribing for them there for several months—and in Wessex (17).) Thus the case load is likely to be disproportionately high in London. The Memorandum suggests that under such circumstances hospitals for the mentally ill and psychiatric departments of general (teaching and non-teaching) hospitals should all participate in this work. The matter is now to be treated as a matter of urgency, hospitals being asked to introduce outpatient services immediately, make provision for their expansion and for the introduction of inpatient facilities at short notice. Hospitals are also requested to prepare and maintain lists of doctors who will eventually need authority to prescribe or supply heroin to addicts. A system for the identification of addicts is shortly to be proposed by the Ministry of Health. The new Dangerous Drugs Bill incorporates most of the suggestions made by the Second Brain Report. Addicts will in future be treated only in special centres. Doctors will be requested to notify the Home Office of addicts. Except when given licence to do so, doctors will be prohibited from prescribing certain drugs, (initially heroin and cocaine) to addicts, although G.P.s will still be able to prescribe such drugs for organic diseases, such as cancer. Stringent penalties, including imprisonment and a heavy fine, are to be applied in the case of doctors who continue to prescribe such drugs to addicts after the Home Secretary—following reference to a panel of doctors and a lawyer—has withdrawn a doctor's licence to prescribe. In view of the number of drug thefts, the Bill may be amended to compel chemists and manufacturers to improve security measures against theft.

The Brain Committee's suggestion that in certain cases compulsory detention should be made possible has been dropped. As in the past, addicts who are unwilling to cease their drug-taking habit will be able to obtain the drugs legally, but only at special maintenance clinics. How far addicts will be willing to avail themselves of this type of facility remains to be seen. Addicts with whom this point was discussed have frequently stated that they would be virtually compelled to live very near such centres as they were fixing several times a day; work would be impossible because of the need to attend so often; they ridiculed the idea of such a clinic being kept open on certain days, for only a few hours. Addicts, typically, are not regular workers anyway, though one aim of any new treatment programme should be to encourage regular working habits. Possibly, newer methods such as the substitution of other drugs (methadone, cyclazorine) and handing over several days' prescription directly to the chemist may help to cut down the number of addicts' attendances at the maintenance clinics. Again, would addicts be willing to attend at a new clinic manned by strange doctors? Possibly the answer to this last question might be that if a number of such clinics were to be opened, the case load for each one of them would not be very large, so that doctors there would be able to get to know their patients, to establish a positive relationship, and in time perhaps to motivate them towards undergoing withdrawal treatment. As in the past in the case of G.P.s, these clinics, too, will find it hard or impossible to assess the needs of patients coming for the first time. Increasing drug tolerance of addicts may present another problem. Certainly the long-term aim of the maintenance clinics should be the really 'therapeutic' one of helping addicts to get off drugs, rather than acting as mere 'dishing-out' centres. Group therapy in these centres would certainly be well worth trying.

The authorities have obviously felt that the risk of an imported large-scale black market (a few cases of attempts at smuggling large amounts of opium into the country have been reported in the Press in recent months) is too real to try more drastic measures of motivating addicts to accept the notion that 'treatment' for drug addiction basically means coming off drugs. In the case of the great majority of addicted youngsters —whose history of drug taking may not be too long—it should, in theory, be feasible to get them, and probably to keep them, off drugs. In other cases, such as those of therapeutic addicts who have been drug dependent for years and may have been able to lead a relatively normal and working life ('stabilized addict'), the regular administration of minimum doses allowing them to carry on as before would seem justified. In any event, the possibility for addicts still to get these drugs legally in the future, even under much restricted circumstances, may, one hopes, obviate the emergence of a large black market; also doctors may be able to motivate more and more of their 'regulars' towards changing their views and agreeing to enter hospital for withdrawal.

The question of staffing these centres raises a number of problems. The important factor is naturally not bricks and mortar, but the quality, experience, human interest, patience and tolerance of the medical, nursing, and other professional staff members. So far, little or no planned attempt has been made at specialized training in this field; the task will become gradually less difficult once there has been more specialized training at the undergraduate level. Again, although psychiatrists see that it may be necessary from a prophylactic 'social' point of view—the prevention of a black market—to prescribe heroin, many of them will find it distasteful to prescribe drugs which they know will cripple the patient's life considerably and hasten his death, often by many years (see Chapter 8). Most would object to having to inject these drugs into patients—as has occasionally been suggested. Addicts, too, for whom the ritual of injecting has often become an important part of the whole process of drug taking, are unlikely to take kindly to such a proposal (cf. p. 39). Addicts will therefore have to be taught the technique of giving themselves injections in a way that does not invite septic complications.

Many questions also attend the proposed new inpatient centres (although a few, such as the Regional Unit of the North West Metropolitan Regional Hospital Board at St. Bernard's Hospital, have been in existence for some years)—questions such as the relative merits of individual and group therapy, of homogeneous (containing addicts only) and heterogeneous (also containing non-addicts) wards, the length to which a permissive regime may be adopted without too great risks, the possible dangers or benefits in mixing various types of addicts in the same ward or establishment. Certainly planned research programmes should be part and parcel of all these proposed projects, including the testing and evaluation of the results obtained with the regime adopted in any particular setting and a comparison of the results obtained with the various regimes.

The value of and the need for research is recognized by the Government as is evident by its proposal to establish an Addiction Research Unit; but many more are needed. Again, there is an urgent need for long-continued, well-planned after-care programmes, incorporating—as should the treatment centres—facilities for vocational training, specialized hostels, etc. An addict's chances are slender indeed if, for example, after discharge from hospital he is to return to the addict sub-culture. As in the case of alcoholics, there is an urgent need for a closely integrated, comprehensive treatment and re-habilitation service to be the responsibility of one clinical director, thus enabling quick transfer and referral of the patient from one facility to another should this become necessary, as it frequently will.

Thus a great many questions remain to be answered; but at

least the State and the community have abandoned their old complacent, laissez-faire attitude as regards this important, modern socio-medical problem. The addict regarded as a sick person who requires help will find a great many friendly, tolerant, understanding and skilled professional helpers by his side. He will be able to look forward to a better, less gloomy, less handicapped, and, less lonely future than in the past, when left more or less to his own devices, the needle and the fix remained virtually his only 'friends'.

REFERENCE

1. *Drug Addiction* (1965) The Second Report of the Interdepartmental Committee. H.M.S.O. London.

Postscript 1968

The number of known (non-professional, non-therapeutic) heroin addicts among the younger age groups continued to rise during 1967, as shown in the revised tables on pages 15 and 18. The total number of known narcotic addicts rose by 380 to 1,729; of these 1,299 used heroin (either alone or in combination with cocaine, methadone or, rarely, with morphine, pethidine or dipipanone), an increase of nearly 50% (400) over the 1966 figure. The number of addicts under 20 years old increased from 329 in 1966 to 395 in 1967 (381 of these being heroin addicts), that of addicts in the 20–34 age group increased even more from 558 (1966) to 906 (1967). The ban on General Practitioners prescribing heroin and cocaine to addicts and the opening of the out-patient centres in the spring of 1968 seemed to gradually decrease the availability of these drugs on the illicit market. This was reflected by the rise in price of illicit heroin, which had been constant for so long at 20s. per grain, but rose to 40s. by the time this postscript was written (November 1968). So far there had been little evidence of any large-scale smuggling of opiates. There have been rumours for some time of so-called 'Chinese heroin' in brownish powder-form being about, and in the last few weeks a number of patients have claimed that they had in fact obtained this stuff in small packets containing about 1–1$\frac{1}{2}$ gr. for which they paid about 20s.–30s.

The finding in the official Home Office statistics for 1967 of addiction among the very young (three heroin addicts aged 15, thirty-eight aged 16, etc.) was reflected in the high proportion of young addicts seen at the out-patient treatment centres.

However, the most striking development in the British drug scene in 1967/68 was the emergence of methylamphetamine* (p. 7) as possibly the most popular drug abused by the young. This development was not wholly unexpected because in the

---

* Methylamphetamine (Methamphetamine) is usually known under its proprietary name 'Methedrine' (cf. p. 7).

history of drug control, the imposition of special restrictions on a particular drug is usually followed by the abuse of other less restricted drugs (p. 107). Even more than in the case of heroin and cocaine, the new epidemic of 'mainlining' methamphetamine seemed to be caused by the indiscriminate overprescribing by a very few General Practitioners who, when no longer entitled to prescribe heroin and cocaine, turned to prescribing methamphetamine. The levelling off of cocaine abuse was already apparent in 1967, followed in 1968 by a marked fall in the number of cocaine abusers. However, in 1968 it became unusual to meet a young drug abuser who did not 'mainline' methamphetamine. Whereas in the preceding years the term '4 and 4' when used by an addict usually signified 4 gr. of heroin and 4 gr. of cocaine, in 1968 it came to mean 4 gr. of heroin and 4 ampoules (30 mg.) of methamphetamine. More rapidly than other amphetamines, methamphetamine injected intravenously produces a high degree of psychological dependence and often a clinical picture that closely simulates paranoid schizophrenia (with feelings of reference, visual and auditory hallucinations). Despite many calls to do something about this new menace, effective steps proved difficult because methylamphetamine is not controlled under the Dangerous Drug Act and could thus not be simply subjected to the new 1967 restrictions affecting heroin and cocaine. However, in October 1968 an agreement was reached between the Ministry of Health, the General Services Committee of the British Medical Association and the manufacturers of the drug that the supply of methylamphetamine ampoules should be restricted to hospitals only, and would no longer be available on prescription. Among the immediate consequences was an increase in the price of these ampoules (up to 40s.) on the illicit market, which in late 1967 and early 1968 had been between 5s. and 7s. 6d per ampoule.

Of the other drugs mentioned in this book, the hashish habit seems to have spread even further (although the clamour for legalizing it seems to have subsided temporarily), but the use of LSD seems to have diminished to some extent.

Glossary

DRUGS

Acid	lysergic acid diethylamide (LSD 25)
Bennies	Benzedrine
Bhang	cannabis (India)
Black bomber	Durophet (amphetamine)
Blue	sodium amytal + drinamyl (any blue tablet)
Blue (French)	Amphetamine/barbiturate mixture
C	cocaine
Charge	cannabis
Coke	cocaine
Dagga	cannabis (S. Africa)
Dex	Dexedrine
Dominoes	Durophet spansules
Freddy	Ephedrine
Gage	cannabis
Ganga	cannabis (W. Indies)
Goof balls	barbiturates
Grass	cannabis
Green and blacks	Librium capsules
H	heroin
Hash	cannabis
Horse	heroin
Jack	heroin tablet
Joint	cannabis cigarette
Kief	cannabis (N. Africa)
Meth	Methedrine
Minstrel (black and white)	Durophet
Pot	cannabis
Purple heart	Drinamyl
Shit	heroin
Sleepers	barbiturates
Speedball	cocaine and heroin together
Spliff	cannabis cigarette

Stuff	Drugs
Sugar	dose of LSD on sugar lump
Tea	cannabis
Weed	cannabis
Zen	LSD

USERS AND METHODS

Acid head	LSD user
Bang	sensation after using (not cocaine)
Blocked	under influence of Drinamyl
Blow	to smoke cannabis
Bug	to annoy or irritate
Burn	smoke
Buzz	stimulating feeling from drug
Caps	capsules
Cold turkey	sudden withdrawal from drugs (usually enforced)
Come down	wearing off of effects of drugs
Connection	drug supplier to individual
Cook up	prepare drug for injection
Crutch	split match used to smoke cannabis cigarette down to the end
Cut	to adulterate drugs
Dry out	slow withdrawal from drugs
Fix	to inject drug
Flash	transient effect of cocaine injection
Flushing	draw up and re-inject blood
Gear	drug-taking equipment. Also own property
Groovy	effects of amphetamines
Habit	dependence
High	under influence of drugs in positive way
Hooked	dependent
Hung up	depressed
Kick	1. thrill, excitement
	2. to give up drugs
Main line	inject intravenously
Nod, nod off	drowsy state after narcotic drugs
Pop (skin)	subcutaneous injection
Pot head	cannabis user
Push	to sell drugs
Raver	one under influence of amphetamine (inexperienced thrill seeker)

Score	to obtain drugs
Scrip	prescription
Shoot up	to inject intravenously
Shot	an injection
Sick	withdrawal symptoms
Spike	hypodermic needle
Stoned	under influence of drugs (cannabis)
Trip	single experience with LSD
Turn on	1. to take drugs
	2. introduce non-user to drugs
Works	syringe and other equipment

ENVIRONMENT

Bird	prison sentence
Bread	money
Busted	to be arrested
Chick	girl
Crazy	enjoyable
Done	caught and punished
Done up	beaten up
Fuzz	police
Gas	amusing
Ginger beer (Queer)	male homosexual
Goof	make a mistake
Hustle	to get together the means to buy drugs
Hustler	street prostitute
John	prostitute's customer
Lesie	female homosexual
Mystery	girl (young) having left home on arrival in London
Pad	room, abode
Scene	addict's environment
Screw	prison officer
Shrinker	psychiatrist
Skipper	to sleep one night and move on
Suss	to suspect
Suss out	to search out another
Trick	single act of intercourse by prostitute
Turn over	1. steal drugs from another addict
	2. to search a room